Topics in
Intermediate
Statistical Methods

VOLUME I

T. A. BANCROFT

Topics in
Intermediate
Statistical Methods

VOLUME I

The Iowa State University Press, Ames, Iowa

T. A. BANCROFT, director of the Statistical Laboratory and head of the Department of Statistics at Iowa State University since 1950, holds the A.B. degree from the University of Florida, the A.M. degree from the University of Michigan, and the Ph.D. degree from Iowa State University. He is past president of Sigma Xi (ISU chapter) and Biometric Society (ENAR); vice-president of the American Statistical Association; a Fellow in the American Association for the Advancement of Science; a Fellow and past member of the board of directors of the American Statistical Association; consultant for the FAO of the United Nations with assignments in Mexico, Egypt, Syria, Iran, Iraq, and India; statistical consultant in Mexico for the Ford and Rockefeller Foundations; a member of the Advisory Committee on Statistical Policy for the U.S. Bureau of the Budget, the National Research Council, the Council of the International Biometric Society, the Econometric Society, the International Association for Statistics in the Physical Sciences, and the Institute of Mathematical Statistics. Besides this book, Dr. Bancroft is co-author of *Statistical Theory in Research*, coeditor of *Statistics and Mathematics in Biology*, author of "Statistics" in the Encyclopedia Americana, and has published numerous articles in scientific and professional journals.

© 1968 The Iowa State University Press
Ames, Iowa, U.S.A. All rights reserved
Printed in U.S.A.
Stock #0842
First edition, 1968
Library of Congress Catalog Card Number 68–17487

TO LENORE

The mind, it appears to me, may divide science into three parts.

The first comprises the most theoretical principles and those more abstract notions whose application is either unknown or very remote.

The second is composed of those general truths that still belong to pure theory, but lead nevertheless by a straight and short road to practical results.

Methods of application and means of execution make up the third.

Each of these different portions of science may be separately cultivated, although reason and experience prove that no one of them can prosper long if it is absolutely cut off from the other two.

ALEXIS DE TOCQUEVILLE, *Democracy in America*

Preface

THE TOPICS selected for Volume I are those that have been found to be of importance to first-year graduate majors in statistics, particularly at a land-grant university, and other graduate students in biology, agriculture, veterinary medicine, medicine and public health, behavioral and social sciences, and certain fields in engineering. An attempt has been made to present a treatment of general intermediate statistical methods rather than specialized methods, for example, in experimental design, survey sampling, economic statistics, and industrial and engineering statistics. Such a general course in intermediate statistical methods should provide background for the more specialized methods courses and complementary training for courses in mathematical and theoretical statistics. Plans have been made to treat other topics in intermediate statistical methods in a similar manner in a subsequent Volume II.

Shortly after Professor George W. Snedecor retired from administrative duties as the founder and first director of the Statistical Laboratory at Iowa State University, it was my good fortune to persuade him to conduct a seminar on statistical methods for first-year graduate students at Iowa State. It was decided to select topics for the seminar which would constitute an extension of the material considered in Professor Snedecor's outstanding text, *Statistical Methods*. At that time he was Queries Editor of *Biometrics* and was receiving numerous requests for answers to questions concerned with increasingly more complicated applications of statistics to actual research situations. It was his wise decision to use these queries as a basis for the new seminar on statistical methods. The seminar met three times a week for one quarter and attracted graduate students majoring in statistics and many others majoring in various substantive fields which make use of statistics as a primary research tool. These students had already taken courses covering most of the material in Snedecor's text and many, particularly the graduate majors in statistics, had taken other graduate level courses in statistics.

When Professor Snedecor left Iowa State in 1958 to make his home in California, it was my pleasant duty to work with other staff members to maintain the strong tradition at Iowa State of emphasis on statistics as a tool for obtaining new knowledge in various substantive fields. Since the methodology of statistics was expanding rapidly, the decision was made to organize a more formal one-quarter course in statistical methods covering certain topics in some depth which were not considered at all, or only introduced, in the basic methods texts. This course was designed as an intermediate statistical methods course and provision was made for a subsequent seminar type course in methods of the type conducted earlier by Professor Snedecor.

Over a period of ten years I have developed and taught the intermediate statistical methods course at Iowa State. It is presently taken by practically all first-year graduate students majoring in statistics. In addition, many graduate students majoring in other fields and minoring in statistics take the course.

I am grateful for the stimulating influence of my colleagues at Iowa State and the patience of my many students who were willing to act as experimental units for the application of repeated revisions. I am also grateful to Mrs. Avonelle Jacobson and Mrs. Judith Donald who brought much patience and skill to the typing of the manuscript.

T. A. Bancroft

Contents

Topics in Intermediate Statistical Methods

VOLUME I

CHAPTER 1

Analysis of Variance: Unequal Subclass Frequencies for Two-Way Classifications

1.1—Introduction. In introductory statistical methods courses the analysis of variance for multiple classified data usually involves an equal number of observations in each subclass. With the usual model assumptions this situation leads to a relatively simple analysis of the data and straightforward inference procedures. Should there be unequal numbers of observations in the subclasses, the analysis and inference procedures are, in general, much more complicated. In this latter case there are exact methods of analysis available which are somewhat lengthy, and there are approximate analytical methods available with accuracy dependent upon the extent of realization of the respective assumptions made for each approximate method.

Since the approximate methods result in a considerable shortening of laborious calculations, they will be particularly useful in cases where the respective assumptions are fairly closely realized and the use of modern computing facilities are not easily available. Such methods are also useful in obtaining preliminary information quickly as to the results to be expected from the exact method of analysis.

The choice of a particular method of analysis and accompanying inferences (tests and estimates) for multiple classified data should depend upon an appropriate model specification. For experimental data the model specification should reflect the manner in which the data are to be obtained (the design of the experiment) and should be made, of course, prior to conducting the experiment. For multiple classified (factorial) treatments arranged in a completely randomized design or analogous situations arising as a part of a more complicated design, and multiple classified nonexperimental data arising, for example, in applying statistical analysis to operational research and to the study of routine data, the model specification and accompanying analysis and inferences should depend upon the kind of partitioning, or stratification into cells, the research worker wishes to assign to the treatment populations to which he wishes to generalize (Tsao, 1946; Norton, 1958). If the investigator does not have the necessary prior information upon which to choose between, say, two alternative possible models, he may wish some assistance from statistical methodology in making such a choice. In this latter situation he may wish to consider inference procedures based on "incompletely specified models" (Bancroft, 1964).

1.2—Notation for multiple classified data. The notation given below is for a general two-way classification in which the subclass numbers may be unequal and disproportionate. It may also be used for the case of equal subclass numbers by setting all $n_{ij} = n$, or for the case of proportionate subclass numbers by setting all $n_{ij} = nu_i v_j$, where $u_1 : u_2 : \ldots : u_r$ are the proportions in the rows and $v_1 : v_2 : \ldots : v_s$ are the proportions in the columns and n is a constant. The extension of the notation for a two-way classification to n-way classifications will be illustrated later for the three-way classification.

TABLE 1.1

TWO-WAY SUBCLASS NUMBERS AND MEANS

B / A	B_1	B_2	$\cdots$	B_j	$\cdots$	B_s	Total
A_1	$y_{11.}(n_{11})$	$y_{12.}(n_{12})$	$\cdots$	$y_{1j.}(n_{1j})$	$\cdots$	$y_{1s.}(n_{1s})$	$y_{1..}(n_{1.})$
A_2	$y_{21.}(n_{21})$	$y_{22.}(n_{22})$	$\cdots$	$y_{2j.}(n_{2j})$	$\cdots$	$y_{2s.}(n_{2s})$	$y_{2..}(n_{2.})$
$\vdots$	$\vdots$	$\vdots$	$\vdots$	$\vdots$	$\vdots$	$\vdots$	$\vdots$
A_i	$y_{i1.}(n_{i1})$	$y_{i2.}(n_{i2})$	$\cdots$	$y_{ij.}(n_{ij})$	$\cdots$	$y_{is.}(n_{is})$	$y_{i..}(n_{is})$
$\vdots$	$\vdots$	$\vdots$	$\vdots$	$\vdots$	$\vdots$	$\vdots$	$\vdots$
A_r	$y_{r1.}(n_{r1})$	$y_{r2.}(n_{r2})$	$\cdots$	$y_{rj.}(n_{rj})$	$\cdots$	$y_{rs.}(n_{rs})$	$y_{r..}(n_{r.})$
Total	$y_{.1.}(n_{.1})$	$y_{.2.}(n_{.2})$	$\cdots$	$y_{.j.}(n_{.j})$	$\cdots$	$y_{.s.}(n_{.s})$	$y_{...}(n_{..})$

The meaning of the symbols in Table 1.1 is as follows:

n_{ij} is the number of observations in the ijth subclass, where $i = 1$, $2, \ldots, r, j = 1, 2, \ldots, s$.

$y_{ij.}$ is the mean of the observations in the (ij)th subclass, where

$$y_{ij.} = \frac{\sum_{k} Y_{ijk}}{n_{ij}} = \frac{Y_{ij.}}{n_{ij}} \quad \text{and} \quad Y_{ijk}$$

is the numerical value of the kth observation in the ith row and jth column.

$n_{i.}$ is the number of observations in A_i, where $n_{i.} = \sum_{j} n_{ij}$.

$y_{i..}$ is the mean of the observations in A_i, where $y_{i..} = \dfrac{\sum_{jk} Y_{ijk}}{n_{i.}}$.

$n_{.j}$ is the number of observations in B_j, where $n_{.j} = \sum_{i} n_{ij}$.

$y_{.j.}$ is the mean of observations in B_j, where $y_{.j.} = \dfrac{\sum_{ik} Y_{ijk}}{n_{.j}}$.

$n_{..}$ is the total number of observations,

$$n_{..} = \sum_{ij} n_{ij} = \sum_{i} n_{i.} = \sum_{j} n_{.j}.$$

$y_{..}$ is the overall mean, $y_{...} = \dfrac{\sum_{ijk} Y_{ijk}}{n_{..}}$.

1.3—General procedure for testing the significance of a set of parameters in a model. In some fields of research it may not be possible to arrange for equal numbers of observations for all treatment combinations of a factorial arrangement. For example, it is not possible to control the treatment combination frequencies on an investigation with turkeys involving, say, three hatches and four breeds. It is assumed that the investigation was undertaken to test whether or not there are significant differences among hatches and among breeds and whether there is evidence of interaction. In such cases the appropriate model specification is that for a factorial arrangement in a completely randomized design with unequal numbers in the subclasses. In the case of replicated experiments with planned equal numbers of observations similar difficulties arise with the analysis when many observations are missing. Procedures to be discussed here are also applicable to this latter case and may be required to give a valid analysis resulting in appropriate inferences.

From the general linear hypothesis theory the technique described in the following is used to obtain a particular sum of squares (SS) for the analysis of Model I (fixed effects model). (This SS will be a function of only one set of the parameters and, hence, makes it possible to test a given hypothesis regarding that set of parameters.) All sets of parameters of the complete model are fitted by least squares and the reduction in total sum of squares computed. Then all but the set of parameters in question are fitted, that is, we assume the set of parameters in question in our model to be zero and compute a second reduction in total sum of squares for this reduced model. The difference between the two is the appropriate reduction in sum of squares attributable only to the differences in the estimates of the parameters of the omitted set.

In the case of a two-way classification with unequal frequencies in the subclasses, the complete model is

$$Y_{ijk} = \mu + \alpha_i + \beta_j + (\alpha\beta)_{ij} + \epsilon_{ijk}, \tag{1.1}$$

where $i = 1, \ldots, r, j = 1, \ldots, s, k = 1, \ldots, n_{ij}$ and the ϵ_{ijk} are independently $\mathcal{N}(0, \sigma^2)$. In order to obtain unique solutions to the subsequent least square equations it is necessary to make assumptions of the form

$$\sum_i c_i\alpha_i = \sum_j d_j\beta_j = \sum_i e_i(\alpha\beta)_{ij} = \sum_j f_j(\alpha\beta)_{ij} = 0, \tag{1.2}$$

where c_i, d_j, e_i, f_j are constants determined by the particular conditions which are imposed upon the parameters.

Let the total unadjusted SS equal

$$\sum_{ijk} Y_{ijk}^2.$$

The reduction in this SS due to fitting model (1.1) is designated as $R(m, a, b, ab)$, where $m, a_i, b_j, (ab)_{ij}$ are respectively the estimates of $\mu, \alpha_i, \beta_j, (\alpha\beta)_{ij}$ in that model. While one could obtain $m, a_i, b_j, (ab)_{ij}$ by least squares and calculate

$$R(m, a, b, ab) = mY_{\ldots} + \sum_i a_iY_{i\ldots} + \sum_j b_jY_{\cdot j\cdot} + \sum_{ij} (ab)_{ij}Y_{ij\cdot},$$

it can be shown that this is exactly equal to the subclass sum of squares, hence, we actually calculate $R(m, a, b, ab)$ as

$$\sum_{ij} \frac{Y_{ij.}^2}{n_{ij}} .$$

As usual, Within Subclass SS = Total SS − Subclass SS. Now, if we wish to test the null hypothesis $H_0 : (\alpha\beta) = 0$, that is, there exists no interaction between the two main effects, then we must fit the reduced model

$$Y_{ijk} = \mu + \alpha_i + \beta_j + \epsilon_{ijk} \tag{1.3}$$

and find $R(m', a', b')$ from

$$R(m', a', b') = m'Y_{...} + \sum_i a_i'Y_{i..} + \sum_j b_j'Y_{.j.} .$$

In general, the numerical values of m and m', a and a', b and b' will not be equal. (Exceptions are the cases of equal and proportional numbers in the subclasses.) Then $R(ab) = R(m, a, b, ab) - R(m', a', b')$. The F-test for significance of the interaction term is

$$F = \frac{R(ab)/(r - 1)(s - 1)}{\text{Within Subclass MS}} \tag{1.4}$$

with $(r - 1)(s - 1)$ and $(n_{..} - rs)$ degrees of freedom, where

$$n_{..} = \sum_{ij} n_{ij} .$$

The procedure described above, and explained for the case of testing the significance of the interaction set of parameters, provides a general method of testing the significance of any particular estimable set of parameters in a linear model.

1.4—Model specification in a two-way classification. The general method described in the previous section will provide unbiased estimates and exact tests of hypothesis if the specified model is appropriate for the investigation in hand. For the two-way classification the appropriate model specification may be (1.1) or (1.3) according as to the presence or not of interaction in the population. If interaction is present in the population but (1.3) has been the model specification, then any main effect sum of squares is only an approximate estimate of the population magnitude of this effect. On the other hand, if interaction is not present in the population, but (1.1) was the model specification, then both of the main effect sum of squares will be unbiased but inefficiently estimated.

In view of the above, and if at all possible, it is desirable to base the choice of model (1.1) or (1.3) on independent prior knowledge regarding the existence or not of interaction in the population. Such prior knowledge may be available from previous independent investigations or from verified theoretical information in the substantive field. Should such independent prior knowledge not be available, the usual practice has been to use the same data to assist the investigator in making an appropriate model specification as well as to handle the subsequent inference problems. This is done by performing a preliminary test of significance on the interaction by calculating an F from formula (1.4). If the F is significant at some preassigned probability level, then model (1.1) is specified and appropriate procedures are then used for testing the significance of the main effects under this particular model assumption. On the other hand, if the F is not significant at the preassigned probability level, then model (1.3) is specified and different procedures are then appropriate for testing the main effects.

The method described in the latter part of the above paragraph falls in the general class designated by the author as methods of analysis for incompletely specified models involving preliminary tests of significance. The difficulty with all such methods is that the final test(s) or estimate(s) are conditional upon the outcome of the preliminary test of significance. Should the effect of performing the preliminary test of significance not be taken into account in making the final test(s) of significance or estimate(s), then the probability levels used in the statements regarding the final test(s) or estimate(s) are not the correct ones.

While some work has been done for related problems (Bozivich, Bancroft, and Hartley, 1956), and additional work is under way on developing adequate methods of analysis for incompletely specified models involving preliminary test of significance, no specific information is available at this time on such matters as bias and mean square error for final estimate(s) or size and power of final test(s) for the problem under discussion (Bancroft, 1953).

In view of the above and in the case of the absence of prior knowledge regarding the presence or absence of interaction, it would seem desirable to assume the complete model (1.1) and perform the test of significance (1.4) of interaction probably at the .25 probability level if the subsequent main effect tests are to be made at the .05 level. This is an exact test. Should the interaction be significant, it may not be desirable to test the main effects since it may be difficult to interpret the results in the face of a significant interaction. On the other hand, if such interpretation should be practically meaningful, the method of weighted squares of means (to be discussed later) should be used to provide tests for the main effects. Should the interaction not be significant, one is faced with a choice of two courses of action, both leading to possible inexact inferences. One could assume that interaction is always present in the population although not necessarily significantly so in the sample, and again use the method of weighted squares of means to test the main effects. Alternatively, one could consider the problem as one involving an incompletely specified model incorporating a preliminary test of significance on interaction. In this latter case and in the face of a nonsignificant interaction, one would then use the method of least squares (fitting constants) to obtain tests of significance for the main effects.

1.5—Equal numbers in the subclasses. If, in a Model I (fixed effects model), the fullest model is assumed, that is, $Y_{ijk} = \mu + \alpha_i + \beta_j + (\alpha\beta)_{ij} + \epsilon_{ijk}$ with the assumptions

$$\sum_i \alpha_i = \sum_j \beta_j = \sum_i (\alpha\beta)_{ij} = \sum_j (\alpha\beta)_{ij} = 0$$

and the ϵ_{ijk} are independently $\mathcal{N}(0, \sigma^2)$, then it can be shown that the different comparisons with which the respective sums of squares are associated are mutually orthogonal and that $R(m, a, b, ab) = R(m) + R(a) + R(b) + R(ab)$. This means that it is very simple to compute the SS for each effect and the interaction since each can be calculated independently of the others. Thus, to find $R(ab)$ it is not necessary to go through the procedure outlined in the general method; a shorter method is available since the addition theorem holds for the sum of squares.

In analyses of variance where the addition theorem holds, it is customary to calculate sums of squares "around the mean" or to "correct for the mean." Since $R(m, a, b, ab) = R(m) + R(a) + R(b) + R(ab)$, then $R(m, a, b, ab) - R(m) = R(a) + R(b) + R(ab) = R(a, b, ab)$. It can be shown that

$$R(m) = mY_{...} = \frac{(Y_{...})^2}{n_{..}}.$$

$R(m)$ will be denoted by CT (correction term), and thus the SS's for A, B, and interaction add up to $R(m, a, b, ab) - CT$, which is the Subclass SS corrected for the mean. The Total SS is also corrected for the mean, giving

$$\text{Total SS} = \sum_{ijk} \Upsilon_{ijk}^2 - CT .$$

As usual, Within SS = Total SS − Subclass SS.

Example 1.1—The following example illustrates the calculations for a two-way AOV with equal numbers of observations in each subclass (Anderson and Bancroft, 1952). Three levels of nitrogen (N) and three levels of phosphate (P) were used to test the fertility of growth of grass on Philadelphia Flat soils in the Manti National Forest. The design was completely randomized with two observations on each treatment combination. Model **I** (fixed effects model) is assumed with interaction present.

TABLE 1.2

GRAMS OF GRASS

P \ N	N_0	N_1	N_2	Total
P_0	18.7 17.5 36.2	20.8 20.5 41.3	22.3 22.9 45.2	122.7
P_1	19.2 21.3 40.5	18.8 23.5 42.3	24.9 24.2 49.1	131.9
P_2	20.8 20.5 41.3	22.0 24.0 46.0	25.6 27.1 52.7	140.0
Total	118.0	129.6	147.0	394.6

Correction Term $= CT = \dfrac{(394.6)^2}{18} = 8650.51 .$

Total SS $= (18.7)^2 + (17.5)^2 + (20.8)^2 + \cdots + (27.1)^2 - CT = 116.35.$

Subclass SS $= \dfrac{(36.2)^2 + (41.3)^2 + \cdots + (52.7)^2}{2} - CT = 98.74 .$

Within (Error) SS = Total SS − Subclass SS = 17.61.

Phosphate SS $= \dfrac{(122.7)^2 + (131.9)^2 + (140.0)^2}{6} - CT = 24.97 .$

Nitrogen SS $= \dfrac{(118.0)^2 + (129.6)^2 + (147.0)^2}{6} - CT = 71.02 .$

NXP Interaction SS = Subclass SS − Phosphate SS − Nitrogen SS = 2.75.

The data are summarized in the following AOV table. The Within MS is the denominator for all F-tests.

TABLE 1.3

Analysis of Variance

Source	df	SS	MS	EMS	F
N	2	71.02	35.51	$\sigma^2 + 6\kappa_n$	18.12**
P	2	24.97	12.49	$\sigma^2 + 6\kappa_p^2$	6.37*
NP	4	2.75	0.69	$\sigma^2 + 2\kappa_{np}^2$	<1
Within	9	17.61	1.96	σ^2	
Total	17	116.35			

**—significant at 1% level.
*—significant at 5% level.

In practice some experimenters, after testing $H_0 : \kappa_{np}^2 = 0$ with an F-test and finding it nonsignificant, advocate pooling the NP SS with the experimental error SS (Within SS) and then dividing by the pooled df to obtain a new experimental error. This new error is then used in testing the other effects. In Example 1.1, since the F-test for interaction is nonsignificant, the pooled error would be

$$\frac{2.75 + 17.61}{4 + 9} = 1.57$$

with 13 df instead of only 9.

The advantage of pooling is that the df for the error mean square is increased. This increases the sensitivity of the final F-test. However, pooling does have its disadvantages. After a preliminary test has been made, that is, $H_0 : \kappa_{np}^2 = 0$, and a decision is made from this test whether to pool or not, the final F-test is no longer being made at the designated α level; in many cases the α level is increased considerably. Paull (1950) states that in some cases a final F-test which the research worker thinks is at the 5% level may be as high as the 47% level.

Ostle (1963) solves the dilemma by advocating a never-pool policy; no matter what the outcome of the F-test for interaction, he recommends that no SS's be pooled to get a new error.

Bozivich, Bancroft, and Hartley (1956) have investigated the actual α level of these final F-tests made after a preliminary F-test for Model II (random effects model) and the mixed model. Although the actual α levels depend upon the ratios of the true mean squares, they have given some general recommendations. Let θ_{21} be defined as the ratio of population Interaction EMS to Within EMS. If the experimenter is reasonably certain that all possible values of θ_{21} are small, then an α level of .25 on the preliminary F-test gives a final F-test which, when made at the 5% level, actually is around the 5% level. Even if θ_{21} is large, the final F-test will still be close to the .05 level, but its power will be diminished.

1.6—Proportional numbers in the subclasses. If the numbers of observations in each subclass are proportional, then n_{ii} can be

represented as nu_iv_j where $u_1, u_2, \ldots, u_r$ are the proportions between rows and $v_1, v_2, \ldots, v_s$ are the proportions between columns, that is, $u_1:u_2: \ldots :u_r, v_1:v_2: \ldots :v_s$. The inferences given
below are valid only if the proportions in the sample are representa-
tive of the population proportions. Let $Y_{ijk} = \mu + \alpha_i + \beta_j + (\alpha\beta)_{ij} + \epsilon_{ijk}$, then the addition theorem for the AOV will hold in
this case also, *if* the following conditions are imposed:

$$\sum_i u_i\alpha_i = \sum_j v_j\beta_j = \sum_i u_i(\alpha\beta)_{ij} = \sum_j v_j(\alpha\beta)_{ij} = 0 .$$

In order to make F-tests, the ϵ_{ijk} are assumed independently $N(0, \sigma^2)$. Thus, since $R(m, a, b, ab) = R(m) + R(a) + R(b) + R(ab)$,
each main effect and interaction can be calculated independently
of the others.

Example 1.2—(Snedecor and Cochran, 1967). The data for a two-
way AOV on dressing percentages (less 70%) of swine is presented below.
The number of observations and total of each subclass is represented in the
two-way table. (Individual observations are given in Snedecor.) Then the
sample subclass numbers are proportional, since $n_{ij} = nu_iv_j$ where $u_1 = 2, u_2 = 1$; $v_1 = 6, v_2 = 15, v_3 = 2, v_4 = 3, v_5 = 5$; $n = 1$. We may check
the proportionality of the n_{ij} in the subclasses in Table 1.4 by use of the
formula

$$n_{ij} = \frac{(n_i.)(n._j)}{n_{..}}, \quad \text{thus} \quad n_{11} = \frac{(62)(18)}{93} = 12 .$$

It is assumed that the proportions in the sample are representative of those
in the population.

TABLE 1.4

SWINE DATA

Sex	Breed					
	1	2	3	4	5	Total
M	168.9 (12)	362.7 (30)	41.6 (4)	79.7 (6)	110.1 (10)	763.0 (62)
F	87.6 (6)	182.7 (15)	27.3 (2)	33.1 (3)	55.7 (5)	386.4 (31)
Total	256.5 (18)	545.4 (45)	68.9 (6)	112.8 (9)	165.8 (15)	1149.4 (93)

$$CT = \frac{(1149.4)^2}{93} = 14205.60 .$$

Total SS $= \sum_{ijk} Y_{ijk}^2 - CT = 580.02$. (Computed from individual obser-

vations.)

Subclass SS $= \dfrac{(168.9)^2}{12} + \dfrac{(362.7)^2}{30} + \cdots + \dfrac{(55.7)^2}{5} - CT = 122.83 .$

Within SS = Total SS − Subclass SS = 457.19 .

$$\text{Breed SS} = \frac{(256.5)^2}{18} + \frac{(545.4)^2}{45} + \cdots + \frac{(165.8)^2}{15} - CT = 97.38 .$$

$$\text{Sex SS} = \frac{(763.0)^2}{62} + \frac{(386.4)^2}{31} - CT = 0.52 .$$

Breed × Sex Interaction = Subclass SS − Breed SS − Sex SS = 24.93.

The data are summarized in the following AOV Table.

TABLE 1.5

ANALYSIS OF VARIANCE

Source	df	SS	MS
Sex	1	0.52	0.52
Breed	4	97.38	24.34
Breed × Sex	4	24.93	6.23
Within	83	457.19	5.51
Total	92	580.02	

Although the sums of squares are easy to compute, a difficulty arises in the EMS for the main effects and interaction due to the unequal numbers of observations in the subclasses. Thus, the F-tests will be more difficult to calculate. Wilk and Kempthorne (1956) have developed general formulas[1] for the EMS for two- and three-factor experiments, and Snedecor and Cochran (1967) present these formulas for a two-factor experiment as follows:

$$A: \sigma^2 + \frac{nuv(1 - u^*)}{a - 1} \left\{ \left(v^* - \frac{1}{B} \right) \sigma_{AB}^2 + \sigma_A^2 \right\} \quad u = \Sigma u, \quad v = \Sigma v$$

$$B: \sigma^2 + \frac{nuv(1 - v^*)}{b - 1} \left\{ \left(u^* - \frac{1}{A} \right) \sigma_{AB}^2 + \sigma_B^2 \right\} \quad u^* = \frac{\Sigma u^2}{(\Sigma u)^2}, \quad v^* = \frac{\Sigma v^2}{(\Sigma v)^2}$$

$$AB: \sigma^2 + \frac{nuv(1 - u^*)(1 - v^*)}{(a - 1)(b - 1)} \sigma_{AB}^2$$

Fixed model: $A = a$, $B = b$; A fixed, B random: $A = a$, $\frac{1}{B} = 0$

Random Model: $\frac{1}{A} = 0$, $\frac{1}{B} = 0$; A random, B fixed: $\frac{1}{A} = 0$, $B = b$.

Using these formulas, the following EMS's are computed:

[1] σ^2 notation is used in the Wilk-Kempthorne general formulas for fixed, random, and mixed models, that is, for all three.

TABLE 1.6

EXPECTED MEAN SQUARES

Source	df	MS	EMS
Sex	1	0.52	$\sigma^2 + 4.58\sigma^2_{AB} + 41.3\sigma^2_A$
Breed	4	24.34	$\sigma^2 + 0.90\sigma^2_{AB} + 16.0\sigma^2_B$
Sex × Breed	4	6.23	$\sigma^2 + 7.11\sigma^2_{AB}$
Within	83	5.51	σ^2

Since both Sex and Breed are fixed, $A = a = 2$, and $B = b = 5$. Then $n = 1$, $u = 2 + 1 = 3$, $v = 6 + 15 + \cdots + 5 = 31$,

$$u^* = \frac{2^2 + 1^2}{3^2} = 0.556, \quad \text{and} \quad v^* = \frac{6^2 + \cdots + 5^2}{31^2} = 0.311 .$$

These values we used in the above formulas to obtain the coefficients of the EMS in Table 1.6. For example,

$$A: \sigma^2 + \frac{(1)(3)(31)}{1}(0.444)\{(.311 - .200)\sigma^2_{AB} + \sigma^2_A\}$$
$$= \sigma^2 + 4.58\sigma^2_{AB} + 41.3\sigma^2_A .$$

The only direct F-test applicable is the test for the Sex-Breed interaction, where $F = 6.23/5.51 = 1.13$, which is nonsignificant. In order to make F-tests for Sex and Breed, an approximate method must be used. One such method is the Satterthwaite-Cochran approximation. The objective is to combine, by addition only, multiples of certain mean squares so that two quantities can be obtained, one of which has an expected value larger than the other only by a multiple of the term which is to be tested. As an example, consider the test for the factor Breed. Take the MS for Sex × Breed and multiply it by .90/7.11 so as to obtain $0.90 \sigma^2_{AB}$ in the EMS for Breeds. Thus,

$$(6.23)\frac{(.90)}{(7.11)} = \frac{.90}{7.11}(s^2 + 7.11s^2_{AB})$$

or
$$0.79 = 0.13s^2 + 0.90s^2_{AB} . \tag{1.5}$$

Comparing (1.5) to

$$24.34 = s^2 + 0.90s^2_{AB} + 16.0s^2_B , \tag{1.6}$$

the coefficients of s^2_{AB} are the same, but are not the same for s^2. So, using the error MS, $5.51 = s^2$, add $s^2 = 5.51$ to (1.5) and add $.13s^2 = 0.72$ to (1.6). This yields:

$$25.06 = 1.13s^2 + 0.90s^2_{AB} + 16.0s^2_B$$
$$6.30 = 1.13s^2 + 0.90s^2_{AB} .$$

Thus,
$$F' = 25.06/6.30 = 3.97 .$$

F' does not follow the F-distribution, but can be approximated by the F-distribution for the following df:

$$\text{Numerator } df = (\text{num, MS})^2 \Big/ \sum_i \frac{[c_i(\text{MS})_i]^2}{f_i},$$

where (num, MS) is the numerator of the F' statistic, $(\text{MS})_i$ is an original MS in the analysis, c_i is the constant multiplier of $(\text{MS})_i$, f_i is the df associated with $(\text{MS})_i$, and the sum is taken over all mean squares added together to give the numerator of the F-test.

$$\text{Denominator } df = (\text{denom. MS})^2 \Big/ \sum \frac{[c_i(\text{MS})_i]^2}{f_i}$$

with analogous definitions for the terms. Thus, in the example considered,

$$\text{numerator } df = (25.06)^2 \Big/ \left[\frac{(0.72)^2}{83} + \frac{(24.34)^2}{4} \right] = 4.2$$

and

$$\text{denominator } df = (6.30)^2 \Big/ \left[\frac{(0.79)^2}{4} + \frac{(5.51)^2}{83} \right] = 76 .$$

Therefore, comparing $F' = 3.97$ to the tabled value of F with 4, 76 df, F is found to be significant at the 1% level.

An alternative procedure, perhaps more appealing computationally, involves combining MS's only for the denominator of the F-test. This involves subtracting MS's as well as adding them together. In the example under discussion, the denominator for the test on Breed should have an EMS of $\sigma^2 + 0.90 \, \sigma^2_{AB}$. This is estimated by estimating its individual components, that is, σ^2 and σ^2_{AB}. The Within Subclass MS yields $\hat{\sigma}^2 = 5.51$. The Interaction MS yields

$$\hat{\sigma}^2 + 7.11 \, \hat{\sigma}^2_{AB} = 6.23$$
$$7.11 \, \hat{\sigma}^2_{AB} = 0.72$$
$$\hat{\sigma}^2_{AB} = .1011 .$$

Thus, $\hat{\sigma}^2 + 0.90 \, \hat{\sigma}^2_{AB} = 5.51 + (0.90)(.1011) = 5.60$.

The test for Breeds is then

$$F' = \frac{24.34}{5.60} = 4.35 .$$

It is necessary to estimate the denominator df. This is done as previously—by finding out from what linear combination of the mean squares the denominator is composed. Denoting Within MS by $(\text{MS})_1$ and Interaction MS by $(\text{MS})_2$ then

$$\hat{\sigma}^2 + 0.90\,\hat{\sigma}^2_{AB} = (MS)_1 + 0.90\left[\frac{(MS)_2 - (MS)_1}{7.11}\right]$$
$$= \left(1 - \frac{.90}{7.11}\right)(MS)_1 + \frac{.90}{7.11}(MS)_2$$
$$= .87(MS)_1 + (.13)(MS)_2 .$$

Thus,

$$\text{denominator } df = (5.60)^2 \left/ \left[\frac{[(.87)(5.51)]^2}{83} + \frac{[(.13)(6.23)]^2}{4}\right]\right. = 71 .$$

Comparing $F' = 4.35$ to the tabulated F with $(4, 71)$ df, Breed is significant at the 1% level.

The question of which of the above procedures to use has been discussed by Cochran (1951). He concludes that when all of the df, f_i, become large, the limiting power functions of the two statistics are the same. In samples of more moderate and practical size, however, the Satterthwaite-Cochran approximation provides an F' which is more nearly F than does the alternative procedure.

The expectations of mean squares, as displayed in Table 1.6, were used above to determine the appropriate calculated F-value or F'-value for exactly or approximately testing a null hypothesis of interest in a fixed effects model. The general formulas displayed above Table 1.6 may also be used for random effects or mixed effects models in the estimation of a variance component of interest. The Wilk-Kempthorne formulas used to obtain the expectations of mean squares in Table 1.6 represent special cases resulting from an attempt to develop general formulas which are applicable to all models (fixed, random, mixed). Note that the notation (σ^2's instead of κ^2's) used in Table 1.6 is for the random effects model, but will be understood here to include the fixed and mixed cases. In deriving the expectation of mean squares Wilk and Kempthorne assumed sampling from finite populations.

1.7—Analysis for two-way classifications with unequal and disproportionate subclass frequencies: exact method applicable to fixed models.
If the two-way classification has unequal and disproportional subclass frequencies, with interaction absent in the model, and an exact analysis is desired, the method of fitting constants is usually used. Short-cut methods are available for the case of two classes of A or two classes of B or both. Only the method applicable to any number of classes of A and B equal to or greater than two will be discussed here. The procedure described is an application of the general method presented in Section 1.3. It will be found that, although the specified model does not contain an interaction term, the least squares sum of squares for the inter-

action of A and B is obtained in a simple, indirect way incidental to the other calculations. A test of significance of the interaction term may then be made as evidence of confirmation or not of the validity of the no-interaction model assumption.

As an aid to subsequent calculations we compute the following preliminary AOV:

TABLE 1.7

PRELIMINARY AOV

Source	df	SS
Subclasses	$rs - 1$	$\sum_{ij} Y_{ij.}^2/n_{ij} - CT$
A, ignoring B	$r - 1$	$\sum_{i} Y_{i..}^2/n_{i.} - CT$
B, ignoring A	$s - 1$	$\sum_{j} Y_{.j.}^2/n_{.j} - CT$
Within subclasses	$n_{..} - rs$	Total SS $-$ Subclass SS
Total	$n_{..} - 1$	$\sum_{ijk} Y_{ijk}^2 - CT$

where the notation is that given in Section 1.2 and

$$CT = \frac{Y_{...}^2}{n_{..}} .$$

The model assumptions for this case are as follows:

$$Y_{ijk} = \mu + \alpha_i + \beta_j + \epsilon_{ijk} , \qquad (1.7)$$
$$i = 1, 2, \ldots, r, \quad j = 1, 2, \ldots, s, \quad k = 1, 2, \ldots, n_{ij} ,$$

and since it is intended to make inferences based on available probability tables, we assume ϵ_{ijk} is NID(0, σ^2). Further, in order to obtain a unique solution of the subsequent least square equations which will arise, the following restrictions are imposed:

$$\sum_{i} \alpha_i = \sum_{j} \beta_j = 0 .$$

It can be shown that the reduction in sum of squares due to fitting all constants in (1.7) is

$$R(m, a, b) = mY_{...} + \sum_{i} a_i Y_{i..} + \sum_{j} b_j Y_{.j.} . \qquad (1.8)$$

We find the estimates $\hat{\mu} = m$, $\hat{\alpha}_i = a_i$, and $\hat{\beta}_j = b_j$ by solving the following:

TABLE 1.8

LEAST SQUARE EQUATIONS

To Estimate Parameters	Equation
m	$n_{..}m + n_{1.}a_1 + n_{2.}a_2 + \cdots + n_{r.}a_r + n_{.1}b_1 + n_{.2}b_2 + \cdots + n_{.s}b_s = Y_{...}$
a_1	$n_{1.}m + n_{1.}a_1 \qquad\qquad\qquad + n_{11}b_1 + n_{12}b_2 + \cdots + n_{1s}b_s = Y_{1..}$
$\vdots$	
a_r	$n_r.m \qquad\qquad\qquad + n_{r.}a_r + n_{r1}b_1 + n_{r2}b_2 + \cdots + n_{rs}b_s = Y_{r..}$
b_1	$n_{.1}m + n_{11}a_1 + \cdots \qquad + n_{r1}a_r + n_{.1}b_1 \qquad\qquad\qquad = Y_{.1.}$
$\vdots$	
b_s	$n_{.s}m + n_{1s}a_1 + \cdots \qquad + n_{rs}a_r \qquad\qquad\qquad\qquad + n_{.s}b_s = Y_{.s.}$

Substituting in (1.8) we find $R(m, a, b)$. Now, we could use the general procedure again to fit the reduced models

$$Y_{ijk} = \mu + \alpha_i + \epsilon_{ijk} \quad \text{and} \quad Y_{ijk} = \mu + \beta_j + \epsilon_{ijk}$$

and hence obtain the reduction in sum of squares due to fitting $\{\mu, \alpha_i\}$ and $\{\mu, \beta_j\}$ respectively.

Again, by fitting $Y_{ijk} = \mu + \epsilon_{ijk}$ we find the reduction due to fitting (μ) only to be

$$\frac{\left(\sum_{ijk} Y_{ijk}\right)^2}{n_{..}} = CT \tag{1.9}$$

Using (1.8) and (1.9) we obtain

$$R(a, b) = \sum_i a_i Y_{i..} + \sum_j b_j Y_{.j.} + mY_{...} - CT. \tag{1.10}$$

Now $R'(a)$, the additional reduction in sum of squares due to fitting $\{\alpha_i\}$, is found by subtracting CT from the reduction in sum of squares due to fitting $\{\mu, \alpha_i\}$; but it can be shown that this is precisely equal to the SS for A, ignoring B given in Table 1.7. One may find $R'(b)$ in a similar manner.

Making use of the above, one could now calculate a final analysis of variance table to test the main effects A and B, assuming no interaction in the model. It was stated earlier, however, that the sum of squares for the interaction of A and B may be obtained in a simple, indirect way incidental to the other calculations and a test of its significance made as evidence of confirmation or not of the validity of the no-interaction model assumption. In order to accomplish this it would appear that one would need to fit the model

$$Y_{ijk} = \mu + \alpha_i + \beta_j + (\alpha\beta)_{ij} + \epsilon_{ijk} ,$$
$$i = 1, 2, \ldots, r, \quad j = 1, 2, \ldots, s, \quad k = 1, 2, \ldots, n_{ij} ,$$
$$\sum_i \alpha_i = \sum_j \beta_j = \sum_i (\alpha\beta)_{ij} = \sum_j (\alpha\beta)_{ij} = 0 ,$$
$$\epsilon_{ij} \sim \text{NID}(0, \sigma^2) ,$$

and find $R[m, a, b, (ab)]$ and hence $R[a, b, (ab)]$. However, it can be shown that $R[a, b, (ab)]$ is precisely equal to the Subclass SS given in Table 1.7. In view of the above it is now possible to calculate a complete AOV, shown in Table 1.9 below, which will include information needed to test the validity of the no-interaction model assumption as well as tests for the main effects. It should be kept in mind that these latter tests are valid only if there is no interaction in the population.

TABLE 1.9

COMPLETE AOV

Source	df	SS	MS
A elim. B	$r - 1$	$R(a, b) - $ SS B ign. $A = R(a)$	$R(a)/(r - 1) = (MS)_A$
B elim. A	$s - 1$	$R(a, b) - $ SS A ign. $B = R(b)$	$R(b)/(s - 1) = (MS)_B$
AB interaction	$(r - 1)$ $(s - 1)$	$R[a, b, (ab)] - R(a, b) = R(ab)$	$R(ab)/(r - 1)(s - 1)$ $= (MS)_{AB}$
Within subclasses	$n.. - rs$	Total SS $-$ Subclass SS $= $ SSE	SSE$/(n.. - rs) = (MS)_E$

The test of significance for interaction, $H_0 : (\alpha\beta) = 0$, for the fixed, random, and mixed cases are performed by calculating

$$F = \frac{(MS)_{AB}}{(MS)_E}$$

from Table 1.9 and comparing it with the tabular F at the desired significance probability level with $(r - 1)(s - 1)$ and $(n.. - rs)$ degrees of freedom, respectively. Whatever the outcome of this test, if the assumption of the no-interaction model is valid, then the test for the main effects for fixed, random, and mixed cases are

(1) H_0: $(\alpha) = 0$,   calculated $F = \dfrac{(MS)_A}{(MS)_E}$,   and

(2) H_0: $(\beta) = 0$,   calculated $F = \dfrac{(MS)_B}{(MS)_E}$.

However, if the assumption of the no-interaction model is not valid, then the estimates $(MS)_A$ and $(MS)_B$ given in Table 1.9 are biased and the above F-tests are not appropriate for testing the main effects. In this latter situation another method, called the Method of Weighted Squares of Means (to be explained later), is available for testing the significance of the main effects.

Example 1.3—The following example illustrates the method of fitting constants for a two-way AOV. Data are quoted by K. A. Brownlee. Quantitative chemical experiments were run to determine the reacting weights of silver (factor A), and iodine (factor B), in Ag I (silver iodide). Five different batches of silver and two different batches of iodine were used in the experiment. These were reacted, and then a determination of the reacting weights was made. The coded data are given in Table 1.10.

TABLE 1.10

CODED REACTING WEIGHTS OF SILVER AND IODINE

A \ B	B_1	B_2	Totals
A_1	22 25 —— 47	−1 40 18 —— 57	104
A_2	41 41 —— 82	23 13 —— 36	118
A_3	29 20 37 —— 86		86
A_4	49 50 —— 99	61 —— 61	160
A_5	55		55
Total	369	154	523

Notice that there are two cells with no observations in them. The method of fitting constants is the only method applicable in this case. Since two interaction terms will not be estimable, the df for interaction is reduced by two.

The model is of Type I, that is,

$$y_{ijk} = \mu + \alpha_i + \beta_j + (\alpha\beta)_{ij} + \epsilon_{ijk} ,$$

where

$$i = 1, 2, 3, 4, 5; \quad j = 1, 2; \quad k = 1, \ldots, n_{ij} .$$

The assumptions relevant to this model and experiment are:

$$\sum_i \alpha_i = \sum_j \beta_j = \sum_i (\alpha\beta)_{ij} = \sum_j (\alpha\beta)_{ij} = 0 \quad \text{and} \quad \epsilon_{ijk} \sim \text{NID}(0, \sigma^2) \,.$$

The preliminary AOV proceeds as follows:

$$CT = \frac{(523)^2}{16} = 17095.5625 \,.$$

$$\text{Total SS} = (22)^2 + \cdots + (55)^2 - CT = 4255.4375 \,.$$

$$\text{Subclass SS} = \frac{(47)^2}{2} + \frac{(57)^2}{3} + \cdots + \frac{(55)^2}{1} - CT = 3213.7708 \,.$$

$$\text{Within SS} = \text{Total SS} - \text{Subclass SS} = 1041.6667 \,.$$

$$A \text{ ignoring } B = \frac{(104)^2}{5} + \cdots + \frac{(55)^2}{1} - CT = 2572.3042 \,.$$

$$B \text{ ignoring } A = \frac{(369)^2}{10} + \frac{(154)^2}{6} - CT = 473.2042 \,.$$

TABLE 1.11

PRELIMINARY ANALYSIS OF VARIANCE

Source	df	SS	MS	F
Subclass	7	3213.7708	459.11	3.53*
A ignoring B	4	2572.3042		
B ignoring A	1	473.2042		
Within (error)	8	1041.6667	130.21	
Total	15			

The F-test for subclasses is significant, indicating a significant silver effect, iodine effect, interaction effect, or any combination of the three possibilities.

Using Table 1.8 the following normal equations are obtained when the model $Y_{ijk} = \mu + \alpha_i + \beta_j + \epsilon_{ijk}$ is assumed:

m	$523 = 16m + 5a_1 + 4a_2 + 3a_3 + 3a_4 + a_5 + 10b_1 + 6b_2$
a_1	$104 = 5m + 5a_1 \qquad\qquad\qquad\qquad\qquad + 2b_1 + 3b_2$
a_2	$118 = 4m \qquad + 4a_2 \qquad\qquad\qquad\qquad + 2b_1 + 2b_2$
a_3	$86 = 3m \qquad\qquad + 3a_3 \qquad\qquad\qquad + 3b_1$
a_4	$160 = 3m \qquad\qquad\qquad\qquad + 3a_4 \qquad + 2b_1 + b_2$
a_5	$55 = m \qquad\qquad\qquad\qquad\qquad + a_5 + b_1$
b_1	$369 = 10m + 2a_1 + 2a_2 + 3a_3 + 2a_4 + a_5 + 10b_1$
b_2	$154 = 6m + 3a_1 + 2a_2 \qquad\quad + a_4 \qquad\qquad + 6b_2 \,.$

The following conditions provide a unique solution to the normal equations:

$$a_1 + a_2 + a_3 + a_4 + a_5 = 0$$
$$b_1 + b_2 = 0 .$$

Methods of solving simultaneous linear equations may be applied to the above equations to obtain a solution for the eight unknowns. Many times, however, the procedure illustrated in Table 1.12 is useful. It eliminates the unknowns of one factor and reduces the normal equations to s equations in s unknowns, where s is the number of levels of the factor which was not eliminated.

Table 1.12 contains the data necessary to write down these equations. (In general, put the factor with the largest number of levels as the rows of the table, for it is the unknowns of this factor which are eliminated in the new equations.) Each cell $(AB)_{ij}$ of Table 1.12 contains the entries

$$n_{ij} \quad \text{and} \quad \frac{n_{ij}}{n_{i.}} .$$

The row mean is $y_{i..}$, where

$$y_{i..} = \frac{Y_{i..}}{n_{i.}} .$$

TABLE 1.12

CALCULATIONS TO OBTAIN REDUCED NORMAL EQUATIONS

A \\ B	B_1	B_2	$n_{i.}$	$Y_{i..}$	$y_{i..}$	$a_i + m$	a_i
A_1	2 .4000	3 .6000	5	104	20.8000	21.5232	−14.3938
A_2	2 .5000	2 .5000	4	118	29.5000	29.5000	−6.4170
A_3	3 1.0000	0 .0000	3	86	28.6667	25.0505	−10.8665
A_4	2 .6667	1 .3333	3	160	53.3333	52.1277	16.2107
A_5	1 1.0000	0 .0000	1	55	55.0000	51.3838	15.4668
$n_{.j}$	10	6	16 = n			179.5852	
$Y_{.j.}$	369	154		523			
b_j	3.6162	−3.6162					

The B_1 equation is obtained by the following scheme:
$$[2(.40) + 2(.50) + 3(1) + 2(.6667) + 1(1) - 10]b_1$$
$$+ [2(.60) + 2(.50) + 3(0) + 2(.3333) + 1(0)]b_2 \tag{1.11}$$
$$= 2(20.80) + 2(29.50) + 3(28.6667) + 2(53.3333) + 1(55) - 369 .$$

The B_2 equation is obtained similarly:

$$[3(.40) + 2(.50) + 0 + 1(.6667) + 0]b_1$$
$$+ [3(.60) + 2(.50) + 0 + 1(.3333) + 0 - 6]b_2 \qquad (1.12)$$
$$= 3(20.80) + 2(29.50) + 0(28.6667) + 1(53.3333) + 0(55.00) - 154 .$$

After simplification (1.11) and (1.12) yield:

$$-2.8666b_1 + 2.8666b_2 = -20.7333 \qquad (1.13)$$
$$2.8667b_1 - 2.8667b_2 = 20.7333 .$$

In general, the matrix of coefficients of the unknowns will be symmetric and of size $s \times s$. The coefficients on any particular unknown, as well as the constants on the right hand side of the equations, sum to zero (except for rounding errors). Only $(s - 1)$ of the s equations will be independent. The other equation comes from the original assumptions—in our case it is

$$b_1 + b_2 = 0 . \qquad (1.14)$$

Solving (1.13) and (1.14) simultaneously gives $b_1 = 3.6162$ and $b_2 = -3.6162$. The b_j's are entered in the last row of the table. The quantities $(m + a_i)$ are calculated using the b_j's, $y_{i.}$'s, and ratios as follows:

$$a_1 + m = 20.8000 - (.4000)(3.6162) - (.6000)(-3.6162) = 21.5232$$
$$a_2 + m = 29.5000 - (.5000)(3.6162) - (.5000)(-3.6162) = 29.5000$$
$$\vdots$$
$$a_5 + m = 55.0000 - (1.0000)(3.6162) - 0(-3.6162) \qquad = 51.3838 .$$

Since

$$\sum_i a_i = 0 ,$$

then

$$\sum_i (a_i + m) = \sum_i m = 5m = 179.5852 .$$

Thus, $m = 35.9170$. Since m is known, each a_i can be calculated by subtracting m from $a_i + m$. The results are in the last column of Table 1.12.

Now it is possible to calculate $R[a, b]$, the reduction in SS due to fitting α_i and β_j.

$$R[a, b] = mY_{...} + \sum_i a_iY_{i..} + \sum_j b_jY_{.j.} - CT$$

$$= (35.9170)(523) + (-14.3938)(104) + \cdots + (15.4668)(55)$$
$$+ (3.6162)(369) + (-3.6162)(154) - 17095.5625 = 2722.2173 .$$

From the preliminary AOV, Table 1.11, the Subclass SS (or $R[a, b, ab]$) is 3213.7708. Thus,

$$SS(AB) = R[ab] = R[a, b, ab] - R[a, b]$$
$$= 3213.7708 - 2722.2173$$
$$= 491.5535.$$

The AB interaction has $4(1) - 2 = 2$ df, since 2 df are subtracted for the two empty cells. Thus, $MS(AB) = 245.78$. The F-test for interaction is

$$F = \frac{MS(AB)}{MS(\text{Within})} = \frac{245.78}{130.21} = 1.89.$$

The tabled value of $F_{.10}(2, 8) = 3.11$, and thus, interaction is not significant at the 10% level.

Now, since it has been assumed that there is no interaction, the usual method of fitting constants may be completed. It remains to calculate the two main effects SS's.

$$SS(A \text{ eliminating } B) = R[a, b] - SS(B \text{ ignoring } A)$$
$$= 2722.2173 - 473.2042$$
$$= 2249.0131.$$
$$SS(B \text{ eliminating } A) = R[a, b] - SS(A \text{ ignoring } B)$$
$$= 2722.2173 - 2572.3042$$
$$= 149.9131.$$

The final AOV is summarized in Table 1.13.

TABLE 1.13

FINAL AOV

Source	df	SS	MS	F
Subclass $= R[a,b,ab]$	7	3213.7708		
A eliminating B	4	2249.0131	562.25	4.32 *
B eliminating A	1	149.9131	149.91	1.15
AB	2	491.5535	245.78	1.89
Within	8	1041.6667	130.21	

Factor A (silver) is significant at the 5% level, whereas B (iodine) is not significant.

It should be remembered that if the method of fitting constants is used, conditional upon a preliminary test $(H_0: (\alpha\beta)_{ij} = 0)$, then the significance level of the tests on main effects may be altered as discussed in Section 1.5. In such cases, in order to control the size and power of the subsequent main effect tests of A, the preliminary test of no interaction should probably be made at the .25 significance level.

1.8—Method of weighted squares of means. If, in a two-way AOV, interaction is present in the model, the method of weighted squares of means, first described by Yates (1934), furnishes unbiased estimates of the main effects. The analysis is carried out on the cell means,

$$y_{ij.} = \frac{\sum\limits_{k} Y_{ijk}}{n_{ij}}.$$

Assume the model $Y_{ijk} = \mu + \alpha_i + \beta_j + (\alpha\beta)_{ij} + \epsilon_{ijk}$ with $i = 1,$ $2, \ldots, r; j = 1, 2, \ldots, s; k = 1, 2, \ldots, n_{ij};$ and $\epsilon_{ijk} \sim$ $\text{NID}(0, \sigma^2)$. Define $y'_{i..}$ and $y'_{.j.}$ as the unweighted row and column means respectively, that is,

$$y'_{i..} = \sum_{j} \frac{y_{ij.}}{s} \quad \text{and} \quad y'_{.j.} = \sum_{i} \frac{y_{ij.}}{r}.$$

On the basis of the assumption of variance homogeneity of the cells, the variance of $y'_{i..}$ is

$$V(y'_{i..}) = V\left(\sum_{j} \frac{y_{ij.}}{s}\right) = \frac{1}{s^2}\left[\sum_{j} V(y_{ij.})\right]$$

$$= \frac{1}{s^2}\sum_{j} \frac{\sigma^2}{n_{ij}} = \frac{\sigma^2}{s^2}\sum_{j} \frac{1}{n_{ij}} = \frac{\sigma^2}{N_i},$$

where

$$\frac{1}{N_i} = \frac{1}{s^2}\sum_{j} \frac{1}{n_{ij}}.$$

These weights N_i will be used in calculating the A main effect SS. The sums of squares for A is defined as

$$(\text{SS})_A = \sum_{i} N_i (y'_{i..} - C)^2,$$

where

$$C = \frac{\left(\sum\limits_{i} N_i y'_{i..}\right)}{\sum\limits_{i} N_i}.$$

It can be shown that

$$\frac{1}{r-1}\sum_{i} N_i(y'_{i..} - C)^2$$

has expectation

$$\sigma^2 + \frac{1}{r-1} \sum_i N_i \alpha_i'^2 ,$$

where

$$\alpha_i' = \alpha_i - \frac{\sum_i N_i \alpha_i}{\sum_i N_i} .$$

The sums of squares for the B effect is defined analogously;

$$(SS)_B = \sum_j N_j (y'_{.j.} - D)^2 ,$$

where

$$\frac{1}{N_j} = \frac{1}{r^2} \sum_i \frac{1}{n_{ij}} \quad \text{and} \quad D = \frac{\sum_j N_j y'_{.j.}}{\sum_j N_j} .$$

Also, under the assumed model,

$$\frac{1}{s-1} \sum_j N_j (y'_{.j.} - D)^2$$

has expectation

$$\sigma^2 + \frac{1}{s-1} \sum_j N_j \beta_j'^2, \quad \text{where} \quad \beta_j' = \beta_j - \frac{\sum_j N_j \beta_j}{\sum_j N_j} .$$

Both main effect mean squares are tested by comparing them against the error (within) mean square. For calculation purposes the following identities are useful:

$$\sum_i N_i (y'_{i..} - C)^2 = \sum_i N_i y'^2_{i..} - \frac{(\Sigma N_i y'_{i..})^2}{\sum_i N_i} \tag{1.15}$$

and

$$\sum_j \mathcal{N}_j(y'_{.j.} - D)^2 = \sum_j \mathcal{N}_j y'^2_{.j.} - \frac{(\Sigma \mathcal{N}_j y'_{.j.})^2}{\sum\limits_j \mathcal{N}_j} . \qquad (1.16)$$

Example 1.4—Weighted squares of means in a two-way AOV. The following data are from Snedecor and Cochran (1967). The observed variable is days-to-death in three strains of mice inoculated with three isolations of the typhoid bacillus. The table below contains the number of observations in each subclass and the mean of each subclass. The model is:

$$Y_{ijk} = \mu + \alpha_i + \beta_j + (\alpha\beta)_{ij} + \epsilon_{ijk},$$
$$i = 1, 2, 3; \quad j = 1, 2, 3; \quad k = 1, 2, \ldots, n_{ij},$$
$$\epsilon_{ijk} \sim \text{NID}(0, \sigma^2).$$

TABLE 1.14

EXPERIMENT WITH MICE

Organism	Strain of Mice		
	RI	Z	Ba
9D	34 4.0000	31 4.0323	33 3.7576
11C	66 6.4545	78 6.7821	113 4.3097
DSC 1	107 6.6262	133 7.8045	188 4.1277

The analysis is started by using the method of fitting constants in order to test for interaction. The preliminary AOV yields:

TABLE 1.15

PRELIMINARY AOV

Source	df	SS	MS	F
Subclasses	8	1785.58	223.20	44.51*
Organism ign. Strain	2	309.47		
Strain ign. Organism	2	1227.19		
Within	774	3881.61	5.015	

The F-test for subclasses is significant at the 1% level, indicating a difference in the subclass means.

The analysis is continued as illustrated previously for the method of fitting constants. After the modified normal equations are obtained and solved, the reduction in SS due to fitting constants is obtained as $R(a, b) =$

1609.78. Thus, Interaction SS = Subclass SS − $R(a, b)$ = 175.80. Interaction MS = $175.80/4$ = 43.95, and the test for interaction yields $F_{4,774}$ = 8.76, which is significant at the 1% level. This is simply a check on the assumption of interaction in the model.

The method of fitting constants cannot be continued in order to investigate main effects; the method of weighted squares of means must be employed. If we had assumed a model with interaction, based on sound prior knowledge, we would still use the method of weighted squares of means even though the test of interaction was not significant. In such case we would attribute the nonsignificant test for interaction to sampling variation. If we had assumed an incompletely specified model, we would, of course, take account of the results of the outcome of the test of interaction in subsequent analysis and inferences.

It is helpful to arrange the calculations for the weighted squares of means in a table similar to the following:

TABLE 1.16

CALCULATIONS FOR WEIGHTED SQUARE OF MEANS

Organism	Strain			$\sum_j 1/n_{ij}$	N_i	$y'_{i..}$	$N_i y'_{i..}$	$N_i y'^{2}_{i..}$
	RI	Z	Ba					
n_{ij} 9D $1/n_{ij}$ $y_{ij.}$	34 .0294 4.0000	31 .0322 4.0323	33 .0303 3.7576	.0919	97.857	3.9300	384.578	1511.392
n_{ij} 11C $1/n_{ij}$ $y_{ij.}$	66 .0152 6.4545	78 .0128 6.7821	113 .0088 4.3097	.0368	244.422	5.8488	1429.575	8361.301
n_{ij} DSCl $1/n_{ij}$ $y_{ij.}$	107 .0093 6.6262	133 .0075 7.8045	188 .0053 4.1277	.0221	405.702 ↑	6.1861	2509.713 ↑	15525.336 ↑
$\sum_i 1/n_{ij}$	.0539	.0525	.0444		Sum 747.981		Sum 4323.866	Sum 25398.029
N_j	166.950	171.108	202.374	540.432 ←Sum				
$y'_{.j.}$	5.6936	6.2063	4.0650					
$N_j y'_{.j.}$	950.547	1061.948	822.650	2835.145 ←Sum				
$N_j y'^{2}_{.j.}$	5412.034	6590.768	3344.072	15346.874 ←Sum				

$$\text{Organism SS} = \sum_i N_i y'^{2}_{i..} - \frac{\left(\sum_i N_i y'_{i..}\right)^2}{\sum_i N_i}$$

$$= 25{,}398.029 - \frac{(4{,}323.866)^2}{747.981}$$

$$= 402.986 \ .$$

$$\text{Strain SS} = \sum_j N_j y_{.j.}^{'2} - \frac{\left(\sum_j N_j y_{.j.}'\right)^2}{\sum_j N_j}$$

$$= 15{,}346.874 - \frac{(2{,}835.145)^2}{540.432}$$

$$= 473.500 \; .$$

TABLE 1.17

COMPLETE AOV

Source	df	SS	MS	F
Organism	2	402.986	201.493	40.18 **
Strain	2	473.500	236.750	47.21 **
Intn.	4	175.800	43.950	8.76 **
Within	774		5.015	

Interpretation of significant main effects when interaction is present must be given careful consideration.

1.9—Summary of exact methods. Given a two-way AOV of size $r \times s$ with unequal and disproportionate subclass numbers, the following working procedure is often used by research workers in the face of uncertainty of the validity of certain model assumptions:

(1) Check the rs cells for homogeneity of variance.
(2) If the variance homogeneity assumption is tenable, test the subclass means for homogeneity;

$$F = \frac{\text{Subclass MS}}{\text{Within MS}} \; .$$

If this is not significant, there may be no need for a further breakdown but such is advisable.

(3) Assuming the subclass means are heterogeneous, begin the method of fitting constants—that is, assume the model $Y_{ijk} = \mu + \alpha_i + \beta_j + \epsilon_{ijk}$ in order to find $R(a, b)$ and, hence, $R(ab)$. Then make an F-test for the interaction component, probably at the .25 significance level, in the model $Y_{ijk} = \mu + \alpha_i + \beta_j + (\alpha\beta)_{ij} + \epsilon_{ijk}$.

(4) If this evidence indicates that interaction is absent, complete the analysis by the method of fitting constants. Contrariwise, complete the analysis by the method of weighted squares of means.

(5) If one or more subclasses are empty, the method of fitting constants must be used to analyze the data regardless of whether interaction is significant or not. The method of weighted squares of means cannot be used since it requires the calculation of the quantities $1/n_{ij}$.

In case the test for interaction should be used as a preliminary test as an aid in specifying the model for subsequent inferences, it is possible to come to an incorrect conclusion, thus making one of two possible mistakes: (1) using the method of fitting constants for estimation of main effects when interaction is present, (2) using the method of weighted squares of means for estimation of main effects when interaction is not present. Mistake (1) may be more drastic, since the main effect mean squares will be biased. Mistake (2) still gives unbiased tests of the main effects, but the main effects will be inefficiently estimated as compared to the method of fitting constants.

If interaction is present, some authors have questioned the usefulness of any analysis, including that of the weighted squares of means, using the argument that the interpretation of main effects cannot be clear in the presence of interaction. Of course, main effects cannot be interpreted in the usual manner; however, in certain investigations the experimenter may well wish to make a main effect test and be able to interpret the outcome for a target or inference population in which interaction does exist (Tsao, 1946; Norton, 1958).

Problems

1.1—An experiment designed to compare eight ration treatments resulted in the following table:

GAINS IN WEIGHT (LBS.) OF FORTY STEERS
FED DIFFERENT RATIONS
(Data Coded for Easy Calculation)

Blocks	Rations									
	T_1	T_1	T_2	T_2	T_3	T_4	T_5	T_6	T_7	T_8
B_1	2	5	4	4	8	6	1	3	8	6
B_2	3	4	5	4	7	5	2	5	8	12
B_3	3	5	6	2	10	5	1	7	7	2
B_4	5	5	3	3	9	2	2	8	8	5

The blocks were outcome groups, that is, the forty steers available for experimental purposes were assigned to the four blocks, 10 in each on the basis of initial weight at the beginning of the experiment. The treatments (rations) were then assigned at random to the steers within each block. Note that treatments 1 and 2 appear *twice* in each block. Obtain an appropriate analysis of variance and test the null hypothesis at the .05 probability level of no difference among the eight population means. Interpret the results.

1.2—The data given below are part of that obtained by Professor Edmond Hoffman at the University of Georgia in 1949. Four breeds of turkeys from three successive hatches two weeks apart were reared to 26 weeks of age. Both sexes were represented and, of course, there were different numbers of survivors from each breed, sex, and hatch. The observations given below in the subclasses are the mean weights and number of birds for the males only. (The male and female data are both given later in Table 3.14.)

MALE SUBCLASS MEANS AND FREQUENCIES

Breed	Hatches			
	H_1	H_2	H_3	Total
B_1	13.17 (18)	14.93 (11)	14.25 (11)	558.00 (40)
B_2	16.41 (22)	16.75 (9)	14.71 (6)	600.00 (37)
B_3	18.79 (17)	21.28 (8)	18.94 (9)	660.20 (34)
B_4	15.91 (26)	18.11 (7)	17.13 (18)	848.50 (51)
Total	1,331.00 (83)	612.00 (35)	723.70 (44)	2,666.70 (162)

Given that the total sum of squares of deviations is 1,315.25, obtain a preliminary analysis of variance table for testing only the Among Subclass Mean Square against the Within Subclass Mean Square at the .05 probability level. Interpret the results.

1.3—Using the data in Problem 1.2 above, obtain appropriate analysis and tests at the .05 probability level for the main effects, given that prior information leads to the assumption of a fixed model with no interaction. Interpret the results.

1.4—Using the data in Problem 1.2 above, obtain appropriate analysis and tests at the .05 probability level for the main effects, given that prior information leads to the assumption of a fixed model with interaction. Interpret the results.

1.5—Using the data in Problem 1.2 above, obtain appropriate analysis and tests at the .05 probability level for the main effects, assuming an incompletely specified fixed model as regards the inclusion or not of an interaction term in the model specification. What about a probability level for the preliminary test of interaction? Comment on the difference between the tests of main effects made here and those made for Problems 1.3 or 1.4 above. Interpret the results.

1.6—Due to the scarcity of experimental animals, one completely randomized experiment was conducted in each of three successive years to compare 6 ration treatments. The results were as follows:

GAINS IN WEIGHT (LBS.)
OF STEERS FED
DIFFERENT RATIONS
(DATA CODED FOR EASY CALCULATION)
Year 1 (Experiment 1)

T_1	T_2	T_3	T_4	T_5	T_6
10	8	3	1	3	2
13	10				
23	18	3	1	3	2

Year 2 (Experiment 2)

T_1	T_2	T_3	T_4	T_5	T_6
15	9	2	3	2	3
		5	2		
15	9	7	5	2	3

Year 3 (Experiment 3)

T_1	T_2	T_3	T_4	T_5	T_6
13	10	3	1	2	3
				4	1
13	10	3	1	6	4

Obtain three separate analyses of variance for testing at the .05 probability level the hypothesis of no treatment difference for each year. Interpret the results.

1.7—Using the results obtained for Problem 1.6 above, test the hypothesis of homogeneity of variance for the three years. Interpret the results.

1.8—Using the data in Problem 1.6 and the results from Problem 1.7 above, explain how one would calculate combined analysis and tests for the three years. Carry out the computations and tests. Discuss three alternative model assumptions. Interpret the results.

References

Anderson, R. L., and T. A. Bancroft. 1952. *Statistical Theory in Research*. McGraw-Hill, Inc., New York.

Bancroft, T. A. 1964. Analysis and inference for incompletely specified models involving the use of preliminary test(s) of significance. *Biometrics* 20:427–442.

———. 1953. Certain approximate formulas for the power and size of a test of a general linear hypothesis incorporating a preliminary test of significance. Iowa State University, unpublished paper prepared for a WADS-sponsored analysis of variance project.

Bozivich, Helen, T. A. Bancroft, and H. O. Hartley. 1956. Power of analysis of variance test procedures for certain incompletely specified models, I. *Annals of Mathematical Statistics* 27:1017–1043.

Cochran, W. G. 1951. Testing a linear relation among variances. *Biometrics* 7:17–32.

Harvey, W. R. 1960. Least-squares analysis of data with unequal subclass numbers. ARS–20–8, USDA Bulletin.

Kempthorne, O. 1952. *The Design and Analysis of Experiments*. John Wiley & Sons, Inc., New York.

Kramer, C. Y. 1955. On the analysis of variance of a two-way classification with unequal subclass numbers. *Biometrics* 441–452.

Nair, K. R. 1940–41. A note on the method of fitting constants for analysis of non-orthogonal data arranged in a double classification. *Sankhya* 5:317–328.

Norton, James. 1958. Influence of weighting choices on tests of main effects and interactions. Purdue University, unpublished paper presented at the Annual Meeting of the American Statistical Association, Chicago, December 27, 1958.

Oktaba, Wiktor. 1962. Mixed models I × J and I × 2 with interaction in the case of non-orthogonal data. Annales Universitatis Mariae Curie-Sklodowska 16:53–75, Lublin, Polonia.

Ostle, Bernard. 1963. *Statistics in Research*. Iowa State University Press, Ames.

Patterson, R. E. 1946. The use of adjusting factors in the analysis of data with disproportionate subclass numbers. *Journal of the American Statistical Association* 41:334–346.

Paull, A. E. 1950. On a preliminary test for pooling mean squares in the analysis of variance. *Annals of Mathematical Statistics* 21:539–556.

Scheffé, Henry. 1956a. A 'mixed model' for the analysis of variance. *Annals of Mathematical Statistics* 27:23–36.

———. 1956b. Alternative models for the analysis of variance. *Annals of Mathematical Statistics* 27:251–271.

————. 1959. *The Analysis of Variance.* John Wiley & Sons, Inc., New York.

Smith, H. F. 1951. Analysis of variance with unequal but proportionate numbers in the subclasses of a two-way classification. *Biometrics* 7:70–74.

Snedecor, George W., and William G. Cochran. 1967. *Statistical Methods.* Iowa State University Press, Ames.

Stevens, W. L. 1948. Statistical analysis of a non-orthogonal tri-factorial experiment. *Biometrika* 35:346–347.

Tsao, Fei. 1942. Tests of statistical hypotheses in the case of unequal or disproportionate numbers of observations in the subclasses. *Psychometrika* 7:195–212.

————. 1946. General solution of the analysis of variance and covariance in the case of unequal or disproportionate numbers of observations in the subclasses. *Psychometrika* 11:107–128.

Wilk, M. B., and O. Kempthorne. 1955. Fixed, mixed and random models. *Journal of the American Statistical Association* 50:1144–1167.

Wilks, S. S. 1938. The analysis of variance and covariance in non-orthogonal data. *Metron* 13:141–154.

Yates, F. 1933. The principal of orthogonality and confounding in replicated experiments. *Journal of Agricultural Science* 23:108.

————. 1934. The analysis of multiple classifications with unequal numbers in the different classes. *Journal of the American Statistical Association* 29:51.

CHAPTER 2

Approximate Methods for a Two-Way Classification With Unequal and Disproportionate Subclass Frequencies

2.1—Introduction. When confronted with nonorthogonal data (unequal and disproportionate subclass frequencies), on occasion the experimenter may not wish to spend the time and/or money on the rather complicated analysis discussed previously, that is, the method of fitting constants or weighted squares of means. For example, he may wish a rather quick approximate analysis while he is awaiting the results of the longer analysis. He seeks some approximate analysis which will be shorter computationally but will still provide reasonably precise results. Two such methods are (1) unweighted means and (2) expected subclass numbers. Both methods make use of the addition theorem for the analysis of variance which holds for orthogonal data and thus make the SS calculations less complicated.

2.2—Method of unweighted means. This method assumes equal frequencies in the subclasses, that is, it gives the same result as the usual orthogonal analysis if there are an equal number of observations in each subclass. If the subclass frequencies do not vary too much among themselves, then this method gives quite accurate results. Its precision decreases as the subclass frequencies vary more and more.

The method of unweighted means is an AOV on the *means* of the subclasses. Since this is analogous to an AOV with one observation per subclass, it can be considered as a special case of equal subclass numbers. Thus, the addition theorem holds here for the SS for the main effects and interaction. These SS's, however, are computed on a "mean" basis, whereas the Within SS (Total SS − Subclass SS) is computed upon an "individual" basis. This Within MS is obviously not the correct one with which to test the main effects and interaction MS's. It must be corrected and put on a "mean" basis to correspond to the MS's for main effects and interaction. This is accomplished by multiplying the Within MS by the reciprocal of the harmonic mean of the frequencies in the subclasses. The multiplying or corrective factor is thus:

$$\frac{1}{\bar{n}_h} = \frac{1}{rs}\left[\frac{1}{n_{11}} + \frac{1}{n_{12}} + \cdots + \frac{1}{n_{rs}}\right]$$

where r is the number of rows, s the number of columns, and n_{ij} the frequency in subclass ij.

Example 2.1—The following Table 2.1 gives the subclass frequencies and the mean interval in days to first heat following parturition of outbred Holstein-Friesian cows having normal calvings.

TABLE 2.1
EXPERIMENT WITH DAIRY COWS
(Parturition $= B$)

Season $= A$	Second	Third	Fourth	Total
Winter	37.962 (26)	39.385 (26)	35.630 (27)	112.977
Spring	33.233 (30)	30.727 (22)	31.179 (28)	95.139
Summer	27.235 (17)	25.722 (18)	31.000 (18)	83.957
Autumn	21.400 (15)	30.091 (11)	28.643 (14)	80.134
Total	119.830	125.925	126.452	372.207

Source: N. C. Buch, W. J. Tyler, and L. E. Casida, "Postpartum estrus and involution of the uterus in an experimental herd of Holstein-Friesian cows," *Journal of Dairy Science*, 38:73–79, 1955.

In this case two models are used. The model for the mean of each subclass is:

$$y_{ij.} = \mu + \alpha_i + \beta_j + (\alpha\beta)_{ij} + \epsilon_{ij.}, \qquad (2.1)$$

where

$$\sum_i \alpha_i = \sum_j \beta_j = \sum_i (\alpha\beta)_{ij} = \sum_j (\alpha\beta)_{ij} = 0, \quad \epsilon_{ij.} = \frac{\displaystyle\sum_k \epsilon_{ijk}}{n_{ij}}$$

and $\epsilon_{ij.} \sim \text{NID}(0, \sigma^2)$. This equation (2.1) is the model which is assumed when the SS for A, B, and AB Interaction are computed. The second model is:

$$Y_{ijk} = \mu + \alpha_i + \beta_j + (\alpha\beta)_{ij} + \epsilon_{ijk}, \tag{2.2}$$

where

$$\sum_i \alpha_i = \sum_j \beta_j = \sum_i (\alpha\beta)_{ij} = \sum_j (\alpha\beta)_{ij} = 0$$

and $\epsilon_{ijk} \sim \text{NID}(0, \sigma_1^2)$. This equation (2.2) is the model which is used when the Within SS is computed. The expectation of the Within MS is σ_1^2, and it must be multiplied by $1/\bar{n}_h$ so that it has expectation σ^2.

The calculations proceed as follows:

Within MS = 246.61 (computed from original observations not present in Table 2.1).

$CT = 11544.838$.

Subclass SS $= (37.962)^2 + (39.385)^2 + \cdots + (28.643)^2 - CT = 285.878$.

$$\text{SS}(A) = \frac{(112.977)^2 + \cdots + (80.134)^2}{3} - CT = 216.985 .$$

$$\text{SS}(B) = \frac{(119.830)^2 + \cdots + (126.452)^2}{4} - CT = 6.773 .$$

SS(AB) = Subclass SS − SS(A) − SS(B) = 62.120.

$1/\bar{n}_h = 1/12(1/26 + 1/30 + 1/17 + \cdots + 1/14) = .05228$.

Error MS = (Within MS)$(1/\bar{n}_h)$ = (246.61)(.05228) = 12.89.

The AOV, assuming a fixed model, is summarized below in Table 2.2.

TABLE 2.2
AOV USING METHOD OF UNWEIGHTED MEANS

Source	df	SS	MS	EMS	F
A	3	216.985	72.33	$\sigma^2 + 3\kappa_A^2$	5.61 **
B	2	6.773	3.39	$\sigma^2 + 4\kappa_B$	<1
AB	6	62.120	10.35	$\sigma^2 + \kappa_{AB}^2$	<1
Error	240		12.89	σ^2	

In case one of the factors is random, the random factor is tested against the error MS and the fixed factor is tested against the AB interaction MS. If both factors are random, they are both tested against the AB interaction MS. In both cases the AB interaction is tested against the error MS.

2.3—Method of expected subclass numbers. If an experiment has resulted in unequal and disproportionate subclass frequencies and the experimenter has reason to believe that the subclass frequencies in the sampled population are proportional, then he may possibly conclude that the subclass frequencies in his experiment should have been proportional. If the reason he did not obtain proportional frequencies can be attributed to sampling variation, then the method of expected subclass numbers may be applied. This method alters the data so that the subclass frequencies are proportional, and then the addition theorem for the AOV holds.

First of all, a χ^2 test is made to verify the assumption that the subclass frequencies in the experiment arose from a population whose subclass frequencies are proportional. If n_{ij} is the frequency of subclass ij in the experiment, then the expected value of n_{ij} is defined as

$$E(n_{ij}) = \frac{(n_{i.})(n_{.j})}{n_{..}} .$$

Thus, given the border totals in the experiment, the experimenter would expect an average subclass frequency of $E(n_{ij})$ in the ijth cell if the population subclass frequencies are truly proportional. χ^2 is then defined as

$$\chi^2 = \sum_i \sum_j \frac{[n_{ij} - E(n_{ij})]^2}{E(n_{ij})}$$

with $(r - 1)(s - 1)$ df. If χ^2 is nonsignificant, the assumption may be tenable, and with this assumption we continue the procedure. If χ^2 is significant, it provides evidence that the experimental subclass frequencies did not come from a proportional population or that the disproportionality in the experimental subclass frequencies did not arise from sampling variation. Thus, the method would not be continued in an effort to test main effects and interaction. It will be noted that this χ^2 test is a preliminary test in the sense noted earlier, and its use strictly speaking will disturb the probability levels of subsequent tests in some unknown way.

Assuming χ^2 to be nonsignificant, compute the Within SS from the original observations as has been demonstrated previously. Then obtain a new total for each subclass by multiplying the subclass mean by $E(n_{ij})$. Thus, each subclass has a new frequency, $E(n_{ij})$, a new total $(y_{ij.})$ $[E(n_{ij})]$. Carry out the usual proportional AOV on this new data. The EMS for main effects and interaction and the resulting significance tests are calculated as discussed in Section 1.6.

Example 2.2—The same data in Example 2.1, which were analyzed by the method of unweighted means, will now be analyzed by the method of expected subclass numbers. The following Table 2.3 contains the observed data (subclass frequencies and means) and the calculated data (expected subclass frequencies and totals).

TABLE 2.3

CALCULATIONS FOR METHOD OF EXPECTED SUBCLASS NUMBERS
(Parturition $= B$)

Season $= A$		Second obs.	prop.	Third obs.	prop.	Fourth obs.	prop.	Total
Winter	n_{ij}	26	27.58	26	24.14	27	27.28	79.00
	$y_{ij.}$		37.962		39.385		35.630	
	$Y_{ij.}$		1046.992		950.754		971.986	2969.732
Spring	n_{ij}	30	27.94	22	24.44	28	27.62	80.00
	$y_{ij.}$		33.233		30.727		31.179	
	$Y_{ij.}$		928.530		750.968		861.164	2540.662
Summer	n_{ij}	17	18.51	18	16.20	18	18.29	53.00
	$y_{ij.}$		27.235		25.722		31.000	
	$Y_{ij.}$		504.120		416.696		566.990	1487.806
Autumn	n_{ij}	15	13.97	11	12.22	14	13.81	40.00
	$y_{ij.}$		21.400		30.091		28.643	
	$Y_{ij.}$		298.958		367.712		395.560	1062.230
$\sum_i n_{ij}$		88.00		77.00		87.00		252
$\sum_i Y_{ij.}$		2778.600		2486.130		2795.700		8060.430

To see if the method of expected subclass numbers is applicable, a preliminary χ^2 test is made. The remarks made above about preliminary tests and in Section 1.4 apply here. A preliminary test (the χ^2 test) is made before the significance tests on the main effects and interaction.

After calculating $E(n_{ij})$ for each cell,

$$\chi^2 = \sum_i \sum_j \frac{[n_{ij} - E(n_{ij})]^2}{E(n_{ij})} = 1.23 .$$

Thus, χ^2, with six df, is nonsignificant, and the method is continued to completion. From the original individual observations (not present in Table 2.3), the Within SS $= 59186.64$.

The following computations are done using the altered data, that is, the expected subclass frequencies and the new subclass totals:

$CT = 257819.570.$

$$\text{Subclass SS} = \frac{(1046.992)^2}{27.58} + \cdots + \frac{(395.560)^2}{13.81} - CT = 5603.904 .$$

$$SS(A) = \frac{(2969.732)^2}{79} + \cdots - CT = 4478.007 .$$

$SS(B) = 23.778$.
$SS(AB) = \text{Subclass SS} - SS(A) - SS(B) = 1102.119$.

The analysis is summarized in Table 2.4.

TABLE 2.4

AOV Using Method of Expected Subclass Numbers

Source	df	SS	MS	EMS
A	3	4478.007	1492.67	$\sigma^2 + c_4 \kappa^2_{AB} + c_5 \kappa^2_A$
B	2	23.778	11.89	$\sigma^2 + c_2 \kappa^2_{AB} + c_3 \kappa^2_B$
AB	6	1102.119	183.69	$\sigma^2 + c_1 \kappa^2_{AB}$
Within	240	59186.64	246.61	σ^2

The c_i values for the EMS entries are obtained using the Wilk-Kempthorne method given in Chapter 1, since we have used the usual proportional AOV on the transformed data. The F-test for AB Interaction is direct, that is,

$$F = \frac{\text{Intn. MS}}{\text{Within MS}}.$$

The F-test for main effects must be approximated by an F'-test (discussed in Section 1.6).

The two different methods of analysis, unweighted means and expected subclass numbers, give about the same results for the example under discussion.

Problems

2.1—Using the data given in Problem 1.2, and assuming a fixed model, obtain approximate analysis of variance and tests using the method of unweighted means. Compare the results with those obtained in Problem 1.3.

2.2—Using the data given in Problem 1.2, and assuming a fixed model, obtain approximate analysis of variance and tests using the method of expected subclass numbers. Compare the results with those obtained in Problems 1.3 and 2.1.

2.3—Using the analysis of variance table, obtained for Problem 2.1 by the method of unweighted means, find the EMS values, assuming (1) a fixed model and (2) a mixed model where Hatch effect is random and Breed effect is fixed.

2.4—Using the data given in Problem 1.6, and assuming treatment effect fixed and year effect random, obtain approximate analysis of variance, EMS values, and tests, using the method of unweighted means. Compare the results with those in Problem 1.6.

References

Anderson, R. L., and T. A. Bancroft. 1952. *Statistical Theory in Research*. McGraw-Hill, Inc., New York.

Bowles, Robert L. 1950. Accuracy of certain approximate methods in predicting the correct model for experiments with unequal frequencies in the subclasses. Unpublished M.S. thesis, Iowa State University, Ames.

Snedecor, George W. 1934. The method of expected numbers for tables of multiple classification with disproportionate subclass numbers. *Journal of the American Statistical Association* 29:389–393.

———, and William G. Cochran. 1967. *Statistical Methods*. Iowa State University Press, Ames.

———, and G. M. Cox. 1935. Disproportionate subclass numbers in tables of multiple classification. Research Bulletin No. 180, Iowa State University, Ames.

Steel, Robert, and James Torrie. 1960. *Principles and Procedures of Statistics*. McGraw-Hill, Inc., New York.

Analysis of Variance: Unequal Subclass Frequencies for Three-Way Classifications

3.1—Introduction. Frequently experimental data may be classified more than two ways—three, four, or n ways. If the subclass frequencies are equal or proportional, the addition theorem for the AOV holds, and the SS calculations can be obtained without too much difficulty. In the case of proportional numbers in the sample, we assume that the proportionality also holds in the population. However, as in the two-way classification, difficulties arise if the subclass frequencies are unequal and disproportionate, since the SS for each effect or interaction is not independent of the others. A general method, which is an extension of fitting constants for a two-way classification, is available if the interactions are zero or nonsignificant. Weighted squares of means can be used to investigate main effects if interactions are assumed present or are significant. The two approximate methods discussed in Chapter 2, unweighted means and expected subclass numbers, can also be extended to three-way and n-way classifications if the data reasonably satisfy the assumptions of these methods.

3.2—Notation for a three-way classification. The notation is a direct extension of that explained in Section 1.2. The lth observation in subclass ijk is denoted by Y_{ijkl}, where $i = 1, 2, \ldots r; j = 1, 2, \ldots s; k = 1, 2, \ldots t;$ and $l = 1, 2, \ldots n_{ijk}$. For equal subclass frequencies $n_{ijk} = n$. For proportional subclass frequencies

$n_{ijk} = nu_i v_j w_k$, where $u_1 : u_2 : \ldots : u_r$ are the proportions in factor A, $v_1 : v_2 : \ldots : v_s$ are the proportions in factor B, $w_1 : w_2 : \ldots : w_t$ are the proportions in factor C, and n is a constant. Table 3.1 displays the usual representation of data which are classified three ways and gives the symbols which are extensions of Table 1.1.

The meaning of the symbols in Table 3.1 is as follows:

n_{ijk} is the number of observations in the ijkth subclass.

$y_{ijk.}$ is the mean of the ijkth subclass, where

$$y_{ijk.} = \frac{\sum\limits_l Y_{ijkl}}{n_{ijk}} = \frac{Y_{ijk.}}{n_{ijk}}.$$

$n_{ij.}$ is the number of observations in $(AB)_{ij}$, where

$$n_{ij.} = \sum\limits_k n_{ijk}.$$

$y_{ij..}$ is the mean of the observations in $(AB)_{ij}$, where

$$y_{ij..} = \frac{\sum\limits_{kl} Y_{ijkl}}{n_{ij.}} = \frac{Y_{ij..}}{n_{ij.}} = \frac{\sum\limits_k Y_{ijk.}}{n_{ij.}}.$$

$n_{i.k}$ is the number of observations in $(AC)_{ik}$, where

$$n_{i.k} = \sum\limits_j n_{ijk}.$$

$y_{i.k.}$ is the mean of the observations in $(AC)_{ik}$, where

$$y_{i.k.} = \frac{\sum\limits_{jl} Y_{ijkl}}{n_{i.k}} = \frac{Y_{i.k.}}{n_{i.k}} = \frac{\sum\limits_j Y_{ijk.}}{n_{i.k}}.$$

$n_{.jk}$ is the number of observations in $(BC)_{jk}$, where

$$n_{.jk} = \sum\limits_i n_{ijk}.$$

$y_{.jk.}$ is the mean of the observations in $(BC)_{jk}$, where

$$y_{.jk.} = \frac{\sum\limits_{il} Y_{ijkl}}{n_{.jk}} = \frac{Y_{.jk.}}{n_{.jk}} = \frac{\sum\limits_i Y_{ijk.}}{n_{.jk}}.$$

TABLE 3.1
Notation for a Three-Way AOV

A_1

	B_1	$\cdots$	B_j	$\cdots$	B_s	Total
C_1	$y_{111.}$ n_{111}	$\cdots$	$y_{1j1.}$ n_{1j1}	$\cdots$	$y_{1s1.}$ n_{1s1}	$y_{1.1.}$ $n_{1.1}$
$\cdots$	$\cdots$	$\cdots$	$\cdots$	$\cdots$	$\cdots$	$\cdots$
C_k	$y_{11k.}$ n_{11k}	$\cdots$	$y_{1jk.}$ n_{1jk}	$\cdots$	$y_{1sk.}$ n_{1sk}	$y_{1.k.}$ $n_{1.k}$
$\cdots$	$\cdots$	$\cdots$	$\cdots$	$\cdots$	$\cdots$	$\cdots$
C_t	$y_{11t.}$ n_{11t}	$\cdots$	$y_{1jt.}$ n_{1jt}	$\cdots$	$y_{1st.}$ n_{1st}	$y_{1.t.}$ $n_{1.t}$
TOTAL	$y_{11..}$ $n_{11.}$	$\cdots$	$y_{1j..}$ $n_{1j.}$	$\cdots$	$y_{1s..}$ $n_{1s.}$	$y_{1...}$ $n_{1..}$

A_i

	B_1	$\cdots$	B_j	$\cdots$	B_s	Total
C_1	$y_{i11.}$ n_{i11}	$\cdots$	$y_{ij1.}$ n_{ij1}	$\cdots$	$y_{is1.}$ n_{is1}	$y_{i.1.}$ $n_{i.1}$
$\cdots$	$\cdots$	$\cdots$	$\cdots$	$\cdots$	$\cdots$	$\cdots$
C_k	$y_{i1k.}$ n_{i1k}	$\cdots$	$y_{ijk.}$ n_{ijk}	$\cdots$	$y_{isk.}$ n_{isk}	$y_{i.k.}$ $n_{i.k}$
$\cdots$	$\cdots$	$\cdots$	$\cdots$	$\cdots$	$\cdots$	$\cdots$
C_t	$y_{i1t.}$ n_{i1t}	$\cdots$	$y_{ijt.}$ n_{ijt}	$\cdots$	$y_{ist.}$ n_{ist}	$y_{i.t.}$ $n_{i.t}$
TOTAL	$y_{i1..}$ $n_{i1.}$	$\cdots$	$y_{ij..}$ $n_{ij.}$	$\cdots$	$y_{is..}$ $n_{is.}$	$y_{i...}$ $n_{i..}$

A_r

	B_1	$\cdots$	B_j	$\cdots$	B_s	Total
C_1	$y_{r11.}$ n_{r11}	$\cdots$	$y_{rj1.}$ n_{rj1}	$\cdots$	$y_{rs1.}$ n_{rs1}	$y_{r.1.}$ $n_{r.1}$
$\cdots$	$\cdots$	$\cdots$	$\cdots$	$\cdots$	$\cdots$	$\cdots$
C_k	$y_{r1k.}$ n_{r1k}	$\cdots$	$y_{rjk.}$ n_{rjk}	$\cdots$	$y_{rsk.}$ n_{rsk}	$y_{r.k.}$ $n_{r.k}$
$\cdots$	$\cdots$	$\cdots$	$\cdots$	$\cdots$	$\cdots$	$\cdots$
C_t	$y_{r1t.}$ n_{r1t}	$\cdots$	$y_{rjt.}$ n_{rjt}	$\cdots$	$y_{rst.}$ n_{rst}	$y_{r.t.}$ $n_{r.t}$
TOTAL	$y_{r1..}$ $n_{r1.}$	$\cdots$	$y_{rj..}$ $n_{rj.}$	$\cdots$	$y_{rs..}$ $n_{rs.}$	$y_{r...}$ $n_{r..}$

$n_{i..}$ is the number of observations in A_i, where

$$n_{i..} = \sum_{jk} n_{ijk} = \sum_{j} n_{ij.} = \sum_{k} n_{i.k} \, .$$

$y_{i...}$ is the mean of the observations in A_i, where

$$y_{i...} = \frac{\displaystyle\sum_{jkl} Y_{ijkl}}{n_{i..}} = \frac{Y_{i...}}{n_{i..}} = \frac{\displaystyle\sum_{j} Y_{ij..}}{n_{i..}} = \frac{\displaystyle\sum_{k} Y_{i.k.}}{n_{i..}} = \frac{\displaystyle\sum_{jk} Y_{ijk.}}{n_{i..}} \, .$$

$n_{.j.}$ is the number of observations in B_j, where

$$n_{.j.} = \sum_{ik} n_{ijk} = \sum_{i} n_{ij.} = \sum_{k} n_{.jk} \, .$$

$y_{.j..}$ is the mean of the observations in B_j, where

$$y_{.j..} = \frac{\displaystyle\sum_{ikl} Y_{ijkl}}{n_{.j.}} = \frac{\displaystyle\sum_{i} Y_{ij..}}{n_{.j.}} = \frac{\displaystyle\sum_{k} Y_{.jk.}}{n_{.j.}} = \frac{\displaystyle\sum_{ik} Y_{ijk.}}{n_{.j.}} = \frac{Y_{.j..}}{n_{.j.}} \, .$$

$n_{..k}$ is the number of observations in C_k, where

$$n_{..k} = \sum_{ij} n_{ijk} = \sum_{i} n_{i.k} = \sum_{j} n_{.jk} \, .$$

$y_{..k.}$ is the mean of the observations in C_k, where

$$y_{..k.} = \frac{\displaystyle\sum_{ijl} Y_{ijkl}}{n_{..k}} = \frac{Y_{..k.}}{n_{..k}} = \frac{\displaystyle\sum_{i} Y_{i.k.}}{n_{..k}} = \frac{\displaystyle\sum_{j} Y_{.jk.}}{n_{..k}} = \frac{\displaystyle\sum_{ij} Y_{ijk.}}{n_{..k}} \, .$$

$n_{...}$ is the total number of observations, where

$$n_{...} = \sum_{ijk} n_{ijk} = \sum_{i} n_{i..} \sum_{j} n_{.j.} = \sum_{k} n_{..k}$$

$$= \sum_{ij} n_{ij.} = \sum_{ik} n_{i.k} = \sum_{jk} n_{.jk} \, .$$

$y_{....}$ is the mean of all the observations, where

$$y_{....} = \frac{\displaystyle\sum_{ijkl} Y_{ijkl}}{n_{...}} = \frac{\displaystyle\sum_{i} Y_{i...}}{n_{...}} = \frac{\displaystyle\sum_{j} Y_{.j..}}{n_{...}} = \frac{\displaystyle\sum_{k} Y_{..k.}}{n_{...}} = \frac{\displaystyle\sum_{ik} Y_{i.k.}}{n_{...}}$$

$$= \frac{\displaystyle\sum_{ij} Y_{ij..}}{n_{...}} = \frac{\displaystyle\sum_{jk} Y_{.jk.}}{n_{...}} = \frac{\displaystyle\sum_{ijk} Y_{ijk.}}{n_{...}} \, .$$

3.3—Equal subclass frequencies. The general procedure discussed in Section 1.3 could be used to obtain an AOV for a model used to describe a three-way classification, but a shorter method is available when the subclass frequencies are equal. Assuming the complete fixed model

$$Y_{ijkl} = \mu + \alpha_i + \beta_j + \gamma_k + (\alpha\beta)_{ij} + (\alpha\gamma)_{ik} + (\beta\gamma)_{jk} \\ + (\alpha\beta\gamma)_{ijk} + \epsilon_{ijkl}, \quad (3.1)$$

where

$$\sum_i \alpha_i = \sum_j \beta_j = \cdots = \sum_k (\alpha\beta\gamma)_{ijk} = 0, \quad \epsilon_{ijkl} \text{ is NID}(0, \sigma^2),$$

the reduction in SS due to fitting Equation (3.1) is denoted by $R[m, a, b, c, ab, ac, bc, abc]$ and it can be shown that

$$R[m, a, b, c, ab, ac, bc, abc] = R(m) + R(a) + R(b) + R(c) \\ + R(ab) + R(ac) + R(bc) \\ + R(abc). \quad (3.2)$$

Thus, each effect and interaction SS can be calculated independently of the others.

The calculations for a three-way AOV are similar to the ones discussed for the two-way classification in Section 1.5, except that the two-factor interactions must be calculated separately as indicated in Example 3.1.

Example 3.1—The data in Table 3.2 are numbers of plants which emerged for three legume species (factor A), three soil types (factor B), and seed either treated or not treated with a fungicide (factor C).[1] The original experiment contained a fourth factor, depth of planting, which was at three levels. For this illustration, however, only the data with a depth level of $\frac{1}{2}$ inch are being used. Blocking was done in the original experiment, but this factor is omitted in the example, and the entry in each subclass of Table 3.2 is a sum of three individual observations.

[1] R. E. Wagner, "Effects of depth of planting and type of soil on the emergence of small-seeded grasses and legumes," M.S. thesis, University of Wisconsin, Madison, 1943; reported in Steel and Torrie, *Principles and Procedures of Statistics*, 1960.

TABLE 3.2

NUMBER OF EMERGED PLANTS

Species = A	Fungicide = C	Soil Type = B		
		Silt Loam = B_1	Sand = B_2	Clay = B_3
Alfalfa = A_1	None = C_1	266	286	66
	Treated = C_2	276	271	215
Red clover = A_2	None = C_1	252	289	167
	Treated = C_2	275	292	203
Sweet clover = A_3	None = C_1	152	197	52
	Treated = C_2	178	219	121

The model is of Type I, that is,

$$Y_{ijkl} = \mu + \alpha_i + \beta_j + \gamma_k + (\alpha\beta)_{ij} + (\alpha\gamma)_{ik} + (\beta\gamma)_{jk} + (\alpha\beta\gamma)_{ijk} + \epsilon_{ijkl},$$

where

$$\sum_i \alpha_i = \sum_j \beta_j = \sum_k \gamma_k = \sum_i (\alpha\beta)_{ij} = \sum_j (\alpha\beta)_{ij} = \sum_i (\alpha\gamma)_{ik}$$

$$= \sum_k (\alpha\gamma)_{ik} = \sum_j (\beta\gamma)_{jk} = \sum_k (\beta\gamma)_{jk} = \sum_i (\alpha\beta\gamma)_{ijk} = \sum_j (\alpha\beta\gamma)_{ijk}$$

$$= \sum_k (\alpha\beta\gamma)_{ijk} = 0 \text{ and } \epsilon_{ijkl} \sim \text{NID}(0, \sigma^2).$$

The calculations proceed as follows:

$$CT = \frac{(3777)^2}{54} = 264180.17.$$

Experiment Total SS = 35597.67 (from individual observations).

Experiment Subclass SS $= \dfrac{(266)^2 + (286)^2 + \cdots + (121)^2}{3} - CT =$ 32041.50.

Within SS = Experiment Total SS − Experiment Subclass SS = 3556.17.

In order to compute main effect and interaction SS's it is helpful to arrange the data in 3 two-way tables. Each table is obtained by summing over the absent classifications. For example, the entry in cell $(AB)_{ij}$ equals

$$\sum_{kl} y_{ijkl}.$$

TABLE 3.3

Two-Way Table for A and B

A \ B	B_1	B_2	B_3	Total
A_1	542	557	281	1380
A_2	527	581	370	1478
A_3	330	416	173	919
Total	1399	1554	824	3777

From this table SS(A), SS(B), and SS(AB) can be computed. Note that six observations go into each entry in Table 3.3.

$$\text{Subclass SS} = \frac{(542)^2 + (557)^2 + \cdots + (173)^2}{6} - CT = 26994.67 .$$

$$\text{SS}(A) = \frac{(1380)^2 + (1478)^2 + (919)^2}{18} - CT = 9900.11 .$$

$$\text{SS}(B) = \frac{(1399)^2 + (1554)^2 + (824)^2}{18} - CT = 16436.11 .$$

$$\text{SS}(AB) = \text{Subclass SS} - \text{SS(A)} - \text{SS(B)} = 658.44 .$$

In Table 3.4 the entry in cell $(BC)_{jk}$ is equal to

$$\sum_{il} Y_{ijkl} .$$

TABLE 3.4

Two-Way Table for B and C

C \ B	B_1	B_2	B_3	Total
C_1	670	772	285	1727
C_2	729	782	539	2050
Total	1399	1554	824	3777

$$\text{Subclass SS} = \frac{(670)^2 + \cdots + (539)^2}{9} - CT = 20219.26 .$$

$$\text{SS}(C) = \frac{(1727)^2 + (2050)^2}{27} - CT = 1932.02 .$$

$$\text{SS}(B) = 16436.11 \text{ (from calculations on Table 3.3) .}$$

$$\text{SS}(BC) = \text{Subclass SS} - \text{SS}(C) - \text{SS}(B) = 1851.14 .$$

In Table 3.5 the entry in cell $(AC)_{ik}$ is equal to

$$\sum_{jl} Y_{ijkl} .$$

TABLE 3.5

Two-Way Table for A and C

C \ A	A_1	A_2	A_3	Total
C_1	618	708	401	1727
C_2	762	770	518	2050
Total	1380	1478	919	3777

Subclass SS $= \dfrac{(618)^2 + \cdots + (518)^2}{9} - CT = 12026.16$.

SS$(A) = 9900.11$ (from calculations on Table 3.3) .

SS$(C) = 1932.02$ (from calculations on Table 3.4) .

SS$(AC) = $ Subclass SS $-$ SS$(A) -$ SS$(C) = 194.03$.

SS$(ABC) = $ Experiment Subclass SS $-$ SS$(A) -$ SS$(B) -$ SS(C)
     $-$ SS$(AB) -$ SS$(AC) -$ SS$(BC) = 1069.65$.

The SS for the ABC interaction can be calculated directly by the following scheme. The direct calculation is not really necessary in a three-way classification, except as a computational check, but the direct method is necessary in classifications having four or more factors. Select the classification with the minimum number of levels—in this case factor C. Set up two-way tables as below by summing over all subscripts not in the table—in this case only l. Each entry is a total of three observations.

TABLE 3.6

C_1

B \ A	A_1	A_2	A_3	Total
B_1	266	252	152	670
B_2	286	289	197	772
B_3	66	167	52	285
Total	618	708	401	1727

TABLE 3.7

C_2

B \ A	A_1	A_2	A_3	Total
B_1	276	275	178	729
B_2	271	292	219	782
B_3	215	203	121	539
Total	762	770	518	2050

$CT = 11046.04$. $CT = 155648.15$.

$(\text{Subclass})_{C_1}\, \text{SS} = 21682.29$. $(\text{Subclass})_{C_2}\, \text{SS} = 8427.18$.

$\text{SS}(A)_{C_1} = 5534.74$. $\text{SS}(A)_{C_2} = 4559.41$.

$\text{SS}(B)_{C_1} = 14659.18$. $\text{SS}(B)_{C_2} = 3628.07$.

$\text{SS}(AB)_{C_1} = 1488.38$. $\text{SS}(AB)_C = 239.71$.

Compute a subclass SS, each main effect SS, and interaction SS for each table. $(AB)_{C_1}$ and $(AB)_{C_2}$ are the two-factor interactions AB at each level of C. Next sum over all levels of C and form a two-way table with A and B. This is, however, the same as Table 3.3. The two-factor interaction AB computed from Table 3.3 is denoted by $(AB)_{C_1+C_2}$ or just AB; the SS for the AB interaction equals 658.44. Now,

$$\begin{aligned}
\text{SS}(ABC) &= \text{SS}(AB)_{C_1} + \text{SS}(AB)_{C_2} - \text{SS}(AB)_{C_1+C_2} \\
&= 1488.38 + 239.71 - 658.44 \\
&= 1069.65 .
\end{aligned}$$

$\text{SS}(ABC)$ could also have been computed by calculating the AC interaction at each level of B or the BC interaction at each level of A, but using the method illustrated resulted in shorter computations.

The AOV is summarized in Table 3.8.

TABLE 3.8

FINAL AOV

Source	df	SS	MS	EMS	F
A	2	9900.11	4500.06	$\sigma^2 + 18\kappa_A^2$	45.56 **
B	2	16436.11	8218.06	$\sigma^2 + 18\kappa_B^2$	83.20 **
C	1	1932.02	1932.02	$\sigma^2 + 27\kappa_C^2$	19.56 **
AB	4	658.44	164.61	$\sigma^2 + 6\kappa_{AB}^2$	1.67
AC	2	194.03	97.02	$\sigma^2 + 9\kappa_{AC}^2$	0.98
BC	2	1851.14	925.57	$\sigma^2 + 9\kappa_{BC}^2$	9.37 **
ABC	4	1069.65	267.41	$\sigma^2 + 3\kappa_{ABC}^2$	2.71 *
Within	36	3556.17	98.78	σ^2	
Total	53	35597.67			

Since the BC or soil $\times$ fungicide interaction is significant, it is desirable to obtain all $C_2 - C_1$ differences in the B by C two-way table. In such case it will be found that this difference is not the same for the b_3, the clay soil type. Since the ABC interaction is also significant, it would seem desirable to examine the BC interactions for each level of A (species).

Different EMS's, and consequently different F-tests, arise if one or more of the factors are random. The calculations, in any case, remain the same. The EMS's for three random factors are shown in Table 3.9. A has a levels, B has b levels, C has c levels, and there are n observations in each cell.

The EMS's in Table 3.9 for the completely random model are arrived at by the following procedure:

(1) Every EMS contains σ^2 and the variation due to the source itself. For example, the EMS for A contains σ^2 and σ_A^2.

(2) Every EMS also contains the variation due to every interaction which includes the source itself. For example, the EMS for A also contains σ_{AB}^2, σ_{AC}^2, and σ_{ABC}^2.

(3) Every term in the EMS has a coefficient. The coefficient of σ^2 is always one. The coefficients of the other terms are obtained by dividing $nabc$ (total number of observations) by the levels of the sources in the term. For example, the coefficient of σ_{AC}^2 is

$$\frac{nabc}{ac} = nb \,.$$

TABLE 3.9

EMS FOR A COMPLETELY RANDOM
THREE-FACTOR FACTORIAL

Source	EMS
A	$\sigma^2 + n\sigma_{ABC}^2 + nc\sigma_{AB}^2 + nb\sigma_{AC}^2 + nbc\sigma_A^2$
B	$\sigma^2 + n\sigma_{ABC}^2 + nc\sigma_{AB}^2 + na\sigma_{BC}^2 + nac\sigma_B^2$
C	$\sigma^2 + n\sigma_{ABC}^2 + nb\sigma_{AC}^2 + na\sigma_{BC}^2 + nab\sigma_C^2$
AB	$\sigma^2 + n\sigma_{ABC}^2 + nc\sigma_{AB}^2$
AC	$\sigma^2 + n\sigma_{ABC}^2 + nb\sigma_{AC}^2$
BC	$\sigma^2 + n\sigma_{ABC}^2 + na\sigma_{BC}^2$
ABC	$\sigma^2 + n\sigma_{ABC}^2$
Within	σ^2

The EMS's for mixed models where some factors are random and some fixed and the EMS's for fixed models can be obtained from the completely random EMS's in Table 3.9. All of the above terms may not appear in the EMS's when there are fixed factors in the experiment. In order to determine whether a particular term enters, first cross out the source under consideration from the subscript of the variation. If any subscripts which are left are fixed, the term does not appear in the EMS. If all of the remaining subscripts are random, the term appears in the EMS. For example, consider the EMS for A when A is fixed, B is fixed, and C is random. σ_{ABC}^2 does not enter into the EMS because when A is deleted, B and C remain, and B is fixed. σ^2_{AB} does not enter into the EMS because when A is deleted, B remains, and B is fixed. σ^2_{AC} does enter because when A is deleted, C remains, and C is random. It is conventional to denote a source of variation by κ^2 instead of σ^2 if all of the subscripts are fixed.

3.4—Proportional subclass frequencies. If the subclass frequencies are proportional, that is, $n_{ijk} = nu_iv_jw_k$, then,

$$R(m, a, b, c, ab, ac, bc, abc) = R(m) + R(a) + R(b) + R(c) + R(ab) \\ + R(ac) + R(bc) + R(abc),$$

and each effect and interaction SS can be calculated independently of the others. Inferences from such an analysis assume that the proportionality in the sample holds in the target population. The calculations parallel those illustrated in Section 3.3 for equal subclass numbers except for the divisors in the SS. A few remarks will suffice to illustrate the alteration in the procedure.

Consider a three-way classification with A at two levels, B at three levels, and C at four levels. Table 3.10 gives the number of observations in each subclass and the total of the observations in each subclass. Some numerical values for n_{ijk} are inserted in order to illustrate the proportionality. Thus, $n_{ijk} = nu_iv_jw_k$, where

$$
\begin{array}{cccc}
u_1 = 1 & v_1 = 1 & w_1 = 1 & n = 1. \\
u_2 = 3 & v_2 = 2 & w_2 = 2 & \\
 & v_3 = 4 & w_3 = 3 & \\
 & & w_4 = 4 &
\end{array}
$$

TABLE 3.10

EXAMPLE OF PROPORTIONAL SUBCLASS FREQUENCIES

A	A_1			A_2			Totals
C $\diagdown$ B	B_1	B_2	B_3	B_1	B_2	B_3	$n_{..k}$
C_1	1 $Y_{111.}$	2 $Y_{121.}$	4 $Y_{131.}$	3 $Y_{211.}$	6 $Y_{221.}$	12 $Y_{231.}$	28
C_2	2 $Y_{112.}$	4 $Y_{122.}$	8 $Y_{132.}$	6 $Y_{212.}$	12 $Y_{222.}$	24 $Y_{232.}$	54
C_3	3 $Y_{113.}$	6 $Y_{123.}$	12 $Y_{133.}$	9 $Y_{213.}$	18 $Y_{223.}$	36 $Y_{233.}$	84
C_4	4 $Y_{114.}$	8 $Y_{124.}$	16 $Y_{134.}$	12 $Y_{214.}$	24 $Y_{224.}$	48 $Y_{234.}$	112
$n_{i..}$	70			210			$n_{...} = 280$

The $n_{.j.}$ are: $n_{.1.} = 40$, $n_{.2.} = 80$, and $n_{.3.} = 160$. We may check the proportionality by use of the formula

$$n_{ijk} = \frac{(n_{i..})(n_{.j.})(n_{..k})}{(n_{...})^2} \ ,$$

thus,

$$n_{111} = \frac{(70)(40)(28)}{(280)^2} = 1 \ .$$

The calculations proceed as follows:

$CT = (Y_{....})^2/n_{....}$.

Total SS is calculated as before.

Experiment Subclass SS $= \sum_{ijk} \dfrac{Y_{ijk.}^2}{n_{ijk}} - CT$.

Within SS $=$ Total SS $-$ Experiment Subclass SS.

The calculations for one of the 3 two-way tables will be demonstrated.

TABLE 3.11

Two-Way Table for A and B

B \ A	A_1	A_2	Total
B_1	$Y_{11..}(n_{11.})$	$Y_{21..}(n_{21.})$	$Y_{.1..}(n_{.1.})$
B_2	$Y_{12..}(n_{12.})$	$Y_{22..}(n_{22.})$	$Y_{.2..}(n_{.2.})$
B_3	$Y_{13..}(n_{13.})$	$Y_{23..}(n_{23.})$	$Y_{.3..}(n_{.3.})$
Total	$Y_{1...}(n_{1..})$	$Y_{2...}(n_{2..})$	$Y_{....}(n_{...})$

Subclass SS $= \sum_i \sum_j \dfrac{Y_{ij..}^2}{n_{ij.}} - CT$.

SS(A) $= \sum_i \dfrac{Y_{i...}^2}{n_{i..}} - CT$.

SS(B) $= \sum_j \dfrac{Y_{.j..}^2}{n_{.j.}} - CT$.

SS(AB) $=$ Subclass SS $-$ SS(A) $-$ SS(B).

The remaining calculations are similar. EMS's are calculated by the method of Wilk and Kempthorne (1955). Approximate F-tests, or F'-tests, are then necessary to test main effects and some of the interactions.

3.5—Exact method applicable to fixed models with unequal and disproportionate subclass frequencies. The exact method has an approach in the three-way classification similar to the approach in the two-way classification. If it can be assumed that all interactions in model (3.1) are zero, then the method of fitting constants may be used to determine the main effect sums of squares by fitting the reduced form of (3.1) without the interaction components. If some interactions in (3.1) may not be assumed zero, then the method of weighted squares of means is used to test main effects. As in the two-way classification, this method is exact if prior knowledge about the interactions is available. Otherwise, the method of investigation of main effects depends upon the outcome of the preliminary test for the interaction terms. In such case one may start by testing the hypothesis that all four interactions, considered together, are simultaneously zero.

The complete model is given by Equation (3.1).

$$R[a,\, b,\, c,\, ab,\, ac,\, bc,\, abc] = \text{Subclass SS} = \sum_{ijk} \frac{Y_{ijk\cdot}^2}{n_{ijk}} - CT,$$

where

$$CT = \frac{Y_{\cdots}^2}{n_{\cdots}}.$$

The reduced model without the interaction terms is:

$$Y_{ijkl} = \mu' + \alpha_i' + \beta_j' + \gamma_k' + \epsilon_{ijkl}'. \tag{3.3}$$

The primes will be omitted below to avoid complicating the notation. The reduction in SS due to fitting model (3.3) is denoted by $R[a,\, b,\, c]$, where the population mean is eliminated as before.

In order to calculate $R[a,\, b,\, c]$ it is necessary to solve the following normal equations:

$$n_{\cdots}m + \sum_i n_{i\cdot\cdot}a_i + \sum_j n_{\cdot j\cdot}b_j + \sum_k n_{\cdot\cdot k}c_k = Y_{\cdots}$$

$$n_{i\cdot\cdot}m + n_{i\cdot\cdot}a_i + \sum_j n_{ij\cdot}b_j + \sum_k n_{i\cdot k}c_k = Y_{i\cdots}$$

$$n_{.j.}m + \sum_i n_{ij.}a_i + n_{.j.}b_j + \sum_k n_{.jk}c_k = Y_{.j..}$$

$$n_{..k}m + \sum_i n_{i.k}a_i + \sum_j n_{.jk}b_j + n_{..k}c_k = Y_{..k..} \qquad (3.4)$$

There are $(r + s + t + 1)$ normal equations, but only $(r + s + t - 2)$ of them are independent. Thus, three additional restrictions are imposed in order that the Equations (3.4) have a unique solution. The conditions are

$$\sum_i a_i = \sum_j b_j = \sum_k c_k = 0 . \qquad (3.5)$$

Equations (3.4) and (3.5) are rather difficult to solve, but with the use of modern computers, this disadvantage of the method may be overcome.

After (3.4) and (3.5) have been solved for the a_i's, b_j's, and c_k's, then

$$R[a, b, c] = mY_{....} + \sum_i a_iY_{i...} + \sum_j b_jY_{.j..} + \sum_k c_kY_{..k.} - CT .$$

$R[a, b, c]$ is then used to obtain $R[ab, ac, bc, abc]$, that is, $R[ab, ac, bc, abc] =$ Subclass SS $- R[a, b, c]$. The preliminary AOV is given in Table 3.12.

TABLE 3.12
Preliminary AOV

Source	df	SS
Subclasses	$rst - 1$	$R[a, b, c, ab, ac, bc, abc] = \sum_{ijk} \dfrac{Y^2_{ijk.}}{n_{ijk}} - CT$
Main effects A, B, and C	$r + s + t - 3$	$R[a, b, c] = mY_{....} + \sum_i a_iY_{i...}$ $+ \sum_j b_jY_{.j..} + \sum_k c_kY_{..k.} - CT$
Interactions AB, AC, BC, and ABC	$rst - r - s - t + 2$	$R[ab, ac, bc, abc] = R[a, b, c, ab, ac, bc, abc]$ $- R[a, b, c]$
Within	$n_{...} - rst$	Total SS $-$ Subclass SS
Total	$n_{...} - 1$	$\sum_{ijkl} Y^2_{ijkl} - CT$

Under the null hypothesis, assuming we wish to use the data to help determine the model, $H_0: (\alpha\beta)_{ij} = (\alpha\gamma)_{ik} = (\beta\gamma)_{jk} = (\alpha\beta\gamma)_{ijk} = 0$, hence

$$\frac{\text{MS (Interactions)}}{\text{MS (Within)}}$$

is distributed as F with $(rst - r - s - t + 2)$ and $(n_{\ldots} - rst)$ df. Thus, the null hypothesis is rejected or accepted according to whether F is significant or not.

Assuming F to be nonsignificant, model (3.3), the purely additive model, is accepted. The main effect SS's—$R[a]$, $R[b]$, $R[c]$—are calculated by fitting further reduced models. For instance, to find $R[a]$ the reduced model

$$Y_{ijkl} = \mu + \beta_j'' + \gamma_k'' + \epsilon''_{kl} \tag{3.6}$$

is fitted. Again, the primes will be dropped in the subsequent discussions. The normal equations for model (3.6) are:

$$Y_{\ldots} = n_{\ldots}m + \sum_j n_{.j.}b_j + \sum_k n_{..k}c_k$$

$$Y_{.j..} = n_{.j.}m + n_{.j.}b_j + \sum_k n_{.jk}c_k \tag{3.7}$$

$$Y_{..k.} = n_{..k}m + \sum_j n_{.jk}b_j + n_{..k}c_k .$$

In order to obtain a unique solution to (3.7), the following conditions are imposed:

$$\sum_j b_j = \sum_k c_k = 0 . \tag{3.8}$$

Notice the similarity of (3.7) and (3.8) to (3.4) and (3.5). The solution to (3.7) and (3.8) for the constants m, b_j, and c_k can be obtained by the method discussed in Example 1.3, Section 1.7. After the system has been solved,

$$R[b, c] = mY_{\ldots} + \sum_j b_j Y_{.j..} + \sum_k c_k Y_{..k.} - CT .$$

Then $R[a] = R[a, b, c] - R[b, c]$.

Analogously, fitting the model

$$Y_{ijkl} = \mu + \alpha_i + \beta_j + \epsilon_{ijkl} \tag{3.9}$$

yields $R[a, b]$ and in turn $R[c]$. Also, fitting the model

$$Y_{ijkl} = \mu + a_i + \gamma_k + \epsilon_{ijkl} \tag{3.10}$$

yields $R[a, c]$ which in turn enables $R[b]$ to be calculated. The final AOV is given in Table 3.13.

TABLE 3.13

Final AOV for Fitting Constants

Source	df	SS	MS
Main effects A, B, and C	$r + s + t - 3$	$R[a, b, c]$	
B and C ignoring A A eliminating B and C	$s + t - 2$ $r - 1$	$R[b, c]$ $R[a] = R[a, b, c] - R[b, c]$	MS(A)
A and C ignoring B B eliminating A and C	$r + t - 2$ $s - 1$	$R[a, c]$ $R[b] = R[a, b, c] - R[a, c]$	MS(B)
A and B ignoring C C eliminating A and B	$r + s - 2$ $t - 1$	$R[a, b]$ $R[c] = R[a, b, c] - R[a, b]$	MS(C)
Within	$n_{...} - rst$	$\sum_{ijkl} Y_{ijkl}^2 - \sum_{ijk} \dfrac{Y_{ijk.}^2}{n_{ijk}}$	E

The mean squares for A, B, and C are compared to the Within MS $= E$ by an F ratio in order to test the three main effects.

Example 3.2—The following table contains subclass means and frequencies of weights of turkeys classified by sex (factor A), breed (factor B), and hatch (factor C). The data were obtained by Professor Edmund Hoffman at the University of Georgia in 1949. Four breeds of turkeys from three successive hatches two weeks apart were raised to 26 weeks of age. Both sexes were represented and, as expected, there were different numbers of survivors from each breed, sex, and hatch. The entry given in each subclass is the respective average weight and number of birds.

TABLE 3.14

Subclass Means and Frequencies

B	B_1		B_2		B_3		B_4	
C \ A	A_1	A_2	A_1	A_2	A_1	A_2	A_1	A_2
C_1	13.17 (18)	8.26 (23)	16.41 (22)	10.70 (20)	18.79 (17)	10.75 (21)	15.91 (26)	10.20 (25)
C_2	14.93 (11)	8.89 (7)	16.75 (9)	10.69 (8)	21.28 (8)	11.94 (4)	18.11 (7)	10.53 (17)
C_3	14.25 (11)	8.98 (10)	14.71 (6)	11.11 (7)	18.94 (9)	12.35 (5)	17.13 (18)	10.40 (17)

$CT = 57561.75$.

Total SS $= 4939.15$ (from original observations) .

Subclass SS $= (18)(13.17)^2 + \cdots + (17)(10.40)^2 - CT = 4071.89$.

Within SS $= 867.26$.

It is now necessary to compute $R[a, b, c]$ using model (3.3), the completely additive model. The normal equations are given by (3.4) and (3.5). By using modern computers or a scheme similar to that used in Example 1.3, and Bowles (1950), the solutions are found to be:

$$
\begin{array}{llll}
m = & 13.5736 & b_1 = & -2.1660 & c_1 = & -.5511 \\
a_1 = & 3.1223 & b_2 = & .1050 & c_2 = & .5314 \\
a_2 = & -3.1223 & b_3 = & 2.0084 & c_3 = & .0197 \\
& & b_4 = & .0526 & &
\end{array}
$$

$$
\begin{aligned}
R[a, b, c] &= R[m, a, b, c] - R[m] \\
&= m Y_{....} + \sum a_i Y_{i...} + \sum_j b_j Y_{.j..} + \sum_k c_k Y_{..k.} - CT \\
&= 3910.08.
\end{aligned}
$$

Table 3.15 gives the preliminary AOV.

TABLE 3.15

PRELIMINARY AOV—FITTING CONSTANTS

Source	df	SS	MS	F
Subclass	23	4071.89		
Main effects A, B, C	6	3910.08		
Interactions AB, AC, BC, and ABC	17	161.81	9.52	3.32**
Within	302	867.26	2.87	
Total	325	4939.15		

The null hypothesis of no interaction is rejected. Ordinarily, the method of fitting constants would not be used to test main effects. If it is used, the SS's for main effects will be biased upwards. However, this example will be completed by the method of fitting constants for two reasons: (1) to illustrate the method and (2) to compare the biased main effect mean squares with the mean squares obtained by the correct method of analysis, the method of weighted squares of means, which is discussed in the next section.

In order to obtain $R[a]$, model (3.6) is fitted, that is,

$$
Y_{ijkl} = \mu + \beta_j + \gamma_k + \epsilon_{ijkl} . \tag{3.6}
$$

This entails solving the normal equations given in (3.7) and (3.8) for m, b_j, and c_k. The following procedure is a good method to use for the solution of the equations. First, set up a two-way table using the factors in the model and summing over the absent classifications. Second, apply the procedure illustrated in Example 1.3—that is, fitting constants in a two-way classification—to the two-way table and solve for the constants. As an illustration, consider the two-way table for (3.6) above.

TABLE 3.16

BREED × HATCH MEANS AND FREQUENCIES

H \ B	B_1	B_2	B_3	B_4	Total $(Y_{..k.})$ $(n_{..k})$
H_1	10.41 (41)	13.69 (42)	14.35 (38)	13.11 (51)	2215.70 (172)
H_2	12.58 (18)	13.90 (17)	18.17 (12)	12.74 (24)	986.54 (71)
H_3	11.74 (21)	12.77 (13)	16.59 (14)	13.86 (35)	1129.63 (83)
Total $(Y_{.j..})$ $(n_{.j.})$	899.79 (80)	977.29 (72)	995.32 (64)	1459.47 (110)	4331.87 (326)

The solution to the normal equations (3.7) and (3.8) using the data in Table 3.16 yields:

$$\begin{aligned} m &= 13.6284 & b_1 &= -2.1866 \\ c_1 &= -.6965 & b_2 &= .1988 \\ c_2 &= .4729 & b_3 &= 2.2016 \\ c_3 &= .2236 & b_4 &= -.2138 \end{aligned}$$

$$\begin{aligned} R[b, c] &= R[m, b, c] - R[m] \\ &= mY_{....} + \sum_j b_j Y_{.j..} + \sum_k c_k Y_{..k.} - CT \\ &= 747.33 . \end{aligned}$$

Thus, $R[a] = R[a, b, c] - R[b, c] = 3910.08 - 747.33 = 3162.75$.

Similarly, by constructing a Sex × Hatch table and a Sex × Breed table, $R[a, c]$ and $R[a, b]$ are computed, from which $R[b]$ and $R[c]$ are then obtained.

The final AOV is summarized in Table 3.17.

TABLE 3.17

FINAL AOV FOR THREE-WAY AOV—FITTING CONSTANTS

Source	df	SS	MS	F
Main effects A, B, C	6	3910.08		
B and C ignoring A	5	747.33		
A eliminating B and C	1	3162.75	3162.75	1102.00 **
A and C ignoring B	3	3280.52		
B eliminating A and C	3	629.56	209.85	73.12 **
A and B ignoring C	4	3847.64		
C eliminating A and B	2	62.44	31.22	10.88 **
Error	302	867.26	2.87	

From the final AOV, all main effects seem highly significant, but it must be remembered that this analysis is really incorrect since it assumes the strictly additive model when interaction is very likely present. Thus, the main effect SS's are biased.

3.6—Weighted squares of means. If, in a three-way AOV, interaction is known to be present in the model, or in an incompletely specified model the test for interaction is significant, the additive model is rejected and (3.1) is accepted. In this case the method of weighted squares of means supplies unbiased mean squares for testing main effects.

The method is a direct extension of the two-way classification. The SS's are defined as follows:

$$\text{SS}(A) = \sum_i N_i(y'_{i...} - c)^2 = \sum_i N_i y'^2_{i...} - \frac{\left(\sum_i N_i y'_{i...}\right)^2}{\sum_i N_i},$$

where

$$\frac{1}{N_i} = \frac{1}{s^2 t^2} \sum_{jk} \frac{1}{n_{ijk}},$$

$$y'_{i...} = \frac{1}{st} \sum_{jk} y_{ijk..},$$

$$c = \frac{\sum_i N_i y'_{i...}}{\sum_i N_i}.$$

$$\text{SS}(B) = \sum_j N_j(y'_{.j.} - d)^2 = \sum_j N_j y'^2_{.j.} - \frac{\left(\sum_j N_j y'_{.j.}\right)^2}{\sum_j N_j},$$

where

$$\frac{1}{N_j} = \frac{1}{r^2 t^2} \sum_{ik} \frac{1}{n_{ijk}},$$

$$y'_{.j..} = \frac{1}{rt} \sum_{ik} y_{ijk.} ,$$

$$d = \frac{\sum_i N_j y'_{.j..}}{\sum_i N_j} .$$

$$\mathrm{SS}(C) = \sum_k N_k (y'_{..k.} - e)^2 = \sum_k N_k y'^{2}_{..k.} - \frac{\left(\sum_k N_k y'_{..k.}\right)^2}{\sum_k N_k} ,$$

where

$$\frac{1}{N_k} = \frac{1}{r^2 s^2} \sum_{ij} \frac{1}{n_{ijk}} ,$$

$$y'_{..k.} = \frac{1}{rs} \sum_{ij} y_{ijk} ,$$

$$e = \frac{\sum_k N_k y'_{..k.}}{\sum_k N_k} .$$

It can be shown, assuming model (3.1), that

$$E[\mathrm{MS}(A)] = \sigma^2 + \frac{1}{r-1} \sum_i N_i \alpha'^2_i, \quad \text{where } \alpha'_i = \alpha_i - \frac{\sum_i N_i \alpha_i}{\sum_i N_i} ,$$

$$E[\mathrm{MS}(B)] = \sigma^2 + \frac{1}{s-1} \sum_j N_j \beta'^2_j, \quad \text{where } \beta'_j = \beta_j - \frac{\sum_j N_j \beta_j}{\sum_j N_j} ,$$

$$E[\mathrm{MS}(C)] = \sigma^2 + \frac{1}{t-1} \sum_k N_k \gamma'^2_k, \quad \text{where } \gamma'_k = \gamma_k - \frac{\sum_k N_k \gamma_k}{\sum_k N_k} ,$$

thus showing that MS(A), MS(B), and MS(C) are unbiased estimates of σ^2 under the null hypothesis of no main effects.

Note that the method of weighted squares of means in no way designates which of the interaction terms out of the four (AB, AC, BC, ABC) are significant. If a finer breakdown of the significant interaction is desired, one may use linear hypothesis theory for estimable components in the full model.

However, the above technique for studying the individual interactions is very laborious since the number of normal equations and unknowns is usually very large. Unless computers are available, it is almost an impossible task. In a case such as this or for preliminary results the experimenter may wish to resort to approximate methods. These are discussed in Chapter 4.

Example 3.3—The data of Example 3.2 will now be analyzed by the method of weighted squares of means. This is the correct analysis, based on an incompletely specified model assumption, since the F-test for interaction in the population is significant.

The preliminary AOV is the same as in Table 3.15. Using the data of Table 3.14, the following quantities are computed for the A effect:

$$\frac{1}{\mathcal{N}_1} = \frac{1}{s^2 t^2} \sum_{jk} \frac{1}{n_{jk}} = \frac{1}{144}\left[\frac{1}{18} + \frac{1}{11} + \frac{1}{11} + \frac{1}{22} + \cdots + \frac{1}{18}\right] = .0075884 .$$

$$\frac{1}{\mathcal{N}_2} = \frac{1}{144}\left[\frac{1}{23} + \frac{1}{7} + \frac{1}{10} + \frac{1}{20} + \cdots + \frac{1}{17}\right] = .0087466 .$$

Thus, $\mathcal{N}_1 = 131.78$ and $\mathcal{N}_2 = 114.33$.

$$y'_{1\ldots} = \frac{1}{12}[13.17 + 14.93 + 14.25 + 16.41 + \cdots + 17.13] = 16.70 .$$

$$y'_{2\ldots} = \frac{1}{12}[8.26 + 8.89 + 8.98 + 10.70 + \cdots + 10.40] = 10.40 .$$

Thus, $SS(A) = \sum_i \mathcal{N}_i y'^2_{i\ldots} - \dfrac{(\Sigma \mathcal{N}_i y'_{i\ldots})^2}{\sum_i \mathcal{N}_i}$

$$= (131.78)(16.70)^2 + (114.33)(10.40)^2 - \frac{[3389.76]^2}{246.11}$$

$$= 2430.10 .$$

Analogously, for the B effect,

$$\begin{array}{ll}
\mathcal{N}_1 = 68.73 & y'_{1..} = 11.41 \\
\mathcal{N}_2 = 56.14 & y'_{2..} = 13.40 \\
\mathcal{N}_3 = 45.43 & y'_{3..} = 15.68 \\
\mathcal{N}_4 = 91.16 & y'_{4..} = 13.71 ,
\end{array}$$

where

$$\frac{1}{\mathcal{N}_1} = \frac{1}{36}\left[\frac{1}{18} + \frac{1}{11} + \frac{1}{11} + \frac{1}{23} + \frac{1}{7} + \frac{1}{10}\right], \text{etc}.$$

$$\mathrm{SS}(B) = \sum_j \mathcal{N}_j y'^2_{.j..} - \frac{\left(\sum_j \mathcal{N}_j y'_{.j..}\right)^2}{\sum_j \mathcal{N}_j} = 516.46.$$

For the C effect,

$$\mathcal{N}_1 = 168.64 \qquad y'_{..1.} = 13.02$$
$$\mathcal{N}_2 = 61.15 \qquad y'_{..2.} = 14.14$$
$$\mathcal{N}_3 = 69.11 \qquad y'_{..3.} = 13.48.$$

$$\mathrm{SS}(C) = \sum_k \mathcal{N}_k y'^2_{..k.} - \frac{\left(\sum_k \mathcal{N}_k y'_{..k.}\right)^2}{\sum_k \mathcal{N}_k} = 57.70.$$

The final AOV is summarized in Table 3.18.

TABLE 3.18

FINAL AOV FOR THREE-WAY AOV—WEIGHTED SQUARES OF MEANS

Source	df	SS	MS	F
A	1	2430.10	2430.10	846.00**
B	3	516.46	172.15	59.98**
C	2	57.70	28.85	10.05**
Interactions AB, AC, BC, ABC	17	161.81	9.52	3.32**
Within	302	867.26	2.87	
Total	325			

Although the same conclusions about the main effects are reached with this analysis as with the incorrect analysis of Example 3.2 (fitting constants), note that every main effect mean square is smaller in this analysis than in the analysis in Table 3.17. This illustrates the bias in the main effect SS's when the method of fitting constants is used and there is interaction in the population.

3.7—Summary of exact methods for a three-way classification.

(1) Check for homogeneity of variance in the subclasses.

(2) If homogeneity assumption is satisfied, test the null hypothesis that all subclass means are equal:

$$F = \frac{\text{Subclass MS}}{\text{Within MS}}.$$

(3) If the subclass means are significant or not, it is customary to investigate main effects.
   (a) If interaction is known to be present in the population, investigate main effects by the method of weighted squares of means.
   (b) If interaction is known not to exist in the population, use the method of fitting constants to test main effects.
   (c) If it is not known whether interaction is present or not, test for it by calculating $R[ab, ac, bc, abc]$. The F-test for interaction is

$$F = \frac{R[ab, ac, bc, abc]}{(rst - r - s - t + 2) \text{ Within MS}}.$$

On the basis of this F-test decide whether interaction is present or absent and proceed as in (a) or (b). Remember, though, that the tests on main effects will not be exactly at the α level because the test for interaction is a preliminary test which precedes the test for main effects. Some preliminary investigations seem to indicate that the preliminary test of significance for interaction should, in general, be made at the .25 significance level to insure the main effect subsequent tests to be at the .05 level.

Problems

3.1—The entries in the first four columns of Table 3.8, Final AOV, for the fixed model will also be used in case of a random or mixed model. Find the EMS entries and F-tests for Table 3.8, if it is assumed that the three legume species are a random sample from a population of legume species appropriate for the agricultural region under consideration. Assume that the soil types and fungicide treatments remain fixed.

3.2—Do the calculations for checking the numerical entries in the Preliminary AOV given in Table 3.15 for the method of fitting constants.

3.3—Do the calculations for checking the numerical entries in the Final AOV given in Table 3.17 for the method of fitting constants.

3.4—Do the calculations for checking the numerical entries in the Final AOV given in Table 3.18 for the method of weighted squares of means.

3.5—Should we decide to let the data assist us in determining the model, that is, place confidence in the outcome of the preliminary test for interaction given in Table 3.15, then the appropriate final AOV should be done by the method of weighted squares of means as shown in Table 3.18. Comment on the possible effect of the preliminary test on the final tests of main effects in Table 3.18.

References

Anderson, R. L., and T. A. Bancroft. 1952. *Statistical Theory in Research*. McGraw-Hill, Inc., New York.

Bowles, Robert L. 1950. Accuracy of certain approximate methods in predicting the correct model for experiments with unequal frequencies in the subclasses. Unpublished M.S. thesis, Iowa State University, Ames.

Snedecor, George W., and William G. Cochran. 1967. *Statistical Methods*. Iowa State University Press, Ames.

Steel, Robert, and James Torrie. 1960. *Principles and Procedures of Statistics*. McGraw-Hill, Inc., New York.

Wilk, M. B., and O. Kempthorne. 1955. Fixed, mixed and random models. *Journal of the American Statistical Association* 50:1144–1167.

CHAPTER 4

Approximate Methods for a Three-Way Classification With Unequal and Disproportionate Subclass Frequencies

4.1—Introduction. As mentioned in Section 3.6, approximate methods are almost a necessity if one does not have access to a computer and still wishes to investigate interactions in a three-way classification. Also, the experimenter may wish to obtain as early as possible some indication from an approximate analysis as to what results may be expected from an exact analysis. The two approximate methods discussed in this chapter are the methods of unweighted means and expected subclass numbers.

4.2—Method of unweighted means. This method for a three-way classification is a direct extension of the procedure discussed in Section 2.2 for the two-way classification.

The Within SS is calculated as usual, that is, Total SS − Subclass SS. For the three-way classification,

$$\frac{1}{\bar{n}_h} = \frac{1}{rst} \sum_{ijk} \frac{1}{n_{ijk}}.$$

The error MS for the experiment is then

$$\frac{\text{Within MS}}{\bar{n}_h}.$$

A table of means is set up, and the SS's for all main effects and interactions are calculated as though the experiment were a three-way classification with one observation per subclass. For the fixed model these MS's are then tested against the error MS for significance.

The method of unweighted means assumes equal numbers in each subclass, and if the experiment deviates widely from this assumption, the method does not give a very good approximation. If desired, a χ^2 test could be made to test the null hypothesis

$$H_0 : E(n_{ijk}) = \mathcal{N}, \quad \text{where} \quad \mathcal{N} = \frac{n_{...}}{rst} .$$

This is analogous to the χ^2 test in the method of expected subclass numbers. If χ^2 is significant, we do not have verification that the method of unweighted means is appropriate.

Example 4.1—The data in Table 3.14 will now be analyzed by the method of unweighted means. From the calculation in Example 3.2, the Within MS $= 2.87$ with 302 df.

$$\frac{1}{\bar{n}_h} = \frac{1}{24} \left[\frac{1}{18} + \frac{1}{11} + \cdots + \frac{1}{17} \right] = .0980 .$$

Thus, Error MS $= (2.87)(.0980) = .2817$.

The main effect and interaction SS's are calculated as shown in detail in Example 3.1 by setting up 3 two-way tables, etc. The results of the analysis are given in Table 4.1, where A, B, and C correspond to the Sex, Breed, and Hatch effects, respectively.

TABLE 4.1

THREE-WAY AOV—UNWEIGHTED MEANS

Source	df	SS	MS	F
Subclasses	23	312.72		
A	1	238.01	238.01	844.91 **
B	3	54.79	18.26	64.82 **
C	2	5.04	2.52	8.95 **
AB	3	7.77	2.59	9.19 **
AC	2	3.04	1.52	5.40 **
BC	6	2.24	.37	1.31
ABC	6	1.83	.31	1.10
Within	302		.2817	

As in the methods of fitting constants and weighted squares of means, all main effects are highly significant. In this analysis, however, additional information is gained in that the specific interactions AB and AC are concluded to be significant. Since interaction is present, main effects interpretation is more difficult. If would seem desirable, in this example, to investigate B and C effects separately for each level of A.

4.3—Method of expected subclass numbers. The procedure here is an extension of that used in the two-way classification. First, a χ^2 test is made to see if the assumptions for a proportional analysis are valid.

$$E(n_{ijk}) = \frac{(n_{i..})(n_{.j.})(n_{..k})}{(n_{...})^2} \text{ and } \chi^2 = \sum_{ijk} \frac{[n_{ijk} - E(n_{ijk})]^2}{E(n_{ijk})}$$

with $(r-1)(s-1)(t-1)$ df. If χ^2 is nonsignificant, $E(n_{ijk})$ is used as the new subclass frequency. $(y_{ijk.})E(n_{ijk})$ is used as the new subclass total, and the main effects and interactions SS's are calculated as in a proportional AOV discussed in Section 3.4. If χ^2 is significant, the assumptions for this approximate analysis are usually considered as not satisfied.

Example 4.2—The data in Table 3.14 will be used again to illustrate the method of expected subclass numbers.

The following tables give n_{ijk}, $E(n_{ijk})$, and $(y_{ijk.})E(n_{ijk})$ for each subclass:

TABLE 4.2

DATA FOR THREE-WAY AOV—EXPECTED SUBCLASS NUMBERS

B		B_1		B_2		B_3		B_4	
A C		A_1	A_2	A_1	A_2	A_1	A_2	A_1	A_2
C_1	n_{ijk}	18	23	22	20	17	21	26	25
	$E(n_{ijk})$	20.97	21.24	18.89	19.12	16.79	16.96	28.84	29.21
	$(y_{ijk.})E(n_{ijk})$	276.175	175.442	309.985	204.584	315.484	182.320	458.844	297.942
C_2	n_{ijk}	11	7	9	8	8	4	7	17
	$E(n_{ijk})$	8.66	8.77	7.79	7.89	6.93	7.01	11.90	12.06
	$(y_{ijk.})E(n_{ijk})$	129.294	77.965	130.482	84.344	147.470	83.699	215.509	126.992
C_3	n_{ijk}	11	10	6	7	9	5	18	17
	$E(n_{ijk})$	10.12	10.26	9.11	9.23	8.11	8.19	13.92	14.07
	$(y_{ijk.})E(n_{ijk})$	144.210	92.135	134.008	102.545	153.603	101.146	238.450	146.328

For this example,

$$\chi^2 = \sum_{ijk} \frac{[n_{ijk} - E(n_{ijk})]^2}{E(n_{ijk})} = \frac{(18 - 20.97)^2}{20.97} + \cdots + \frac{(17 - 14.07)^2}{14.07}$$

$$= 14.49 \text{ with } 6 \text{ } df.$$

This χ^2 is significant at the 5% level, which implies that a proportional analysis would not be considered appropriate. However, the analysis will be continued in order to illustrate the method and to compare the results with the other methods which have been used on this data.

One of the 3 two-way tables is given below, and the corresponding calculations are illustrated.

TABLE 4.3

TWO-WAY TABLE FOR SEX AND BREED

			Totals and Subclass Frequencies			
B A		B_1	B_2	B_3	B_4	Total
A_1	$n_{ij.}$ $Y_{ij..}$	39.75 549.679	35.79 574.475	31.83 616.557	54.66 912.803	162.03 2653.514
A_2	$n_{ij.}$ $Y_{ij..}$	40.27 345.542	36.24 391.473	32.16 367.165	55.34 571.262	164.01 1675.442
Total		80.02 895.221	72.03 965.948	63.99 983.722	110.00 1484.065	326.04 4328.956

$CT = (4328.956)^2/326.04 .$

$$\text{Subclass SS} = \frac{(549.679)^2}{39.75} + \cdots + \frac{(571.262)^2}{55.34} - CT = 3812.64 .$$

$$SS(A) = \frac{(2653.514)^2}{162.03} + \frac{(1675.442)^2}{164.01} - CT = 3092.79 .$$

$$SS(B) = \frac{(895.221)^2}{80.02} + \cdots + \frac{(1484.065)^2}{110.00} - CT = 635.49 .$$

$SS(AB) = \text{Subclass SS} - SS(A) - SS(B) = 84.36 .$

The final AOV is given in Table 4.4.

TABLE 4.4

FINAL AOV—EXPECTED SUBCLASS NUMBERS

Source	df	SS	MS
A	1	3092.79	3092.8 **
B	3	635.49	211.8 **
C	2	64.05	32.0 **
AB	3	84.36	28.1 **
AC	2	26.51	13.3 **
BC	6	28.77	4.8
ABC	6	24.82	4.1
Within	302	867.26	2.87

F-tests are made by the method discussed in Section 1.6 after the EMS's are obtained for each source. Conclusions of this method agree with those of the method of unweighted means.

Problems

4.1—Check the calculations for obtaining the entries in the AOV given in Table 4.1.

4.2—Since the Sex × Breed (*AB*) and the Sex × Hatch (*AC*) interactions are significant and the Breed × Hatch interaction is not significant, it was suggested in Section 4.2 that it would seem advisable to investigate the Breed and Hatch effects separately for each sex. Obtain a separate approximate analysis of variance for males and females using the method of unweighted means and assuming a fixed model for each. Interpret the results for tests of main effects and interactions made separately for males and females. Compare the results and inferences for each.

4.3—In Table 4.1 assume that the Hatch effect is random while the Sex and Breed effects are still fixed. Find the EMS for each line in the AOV table, for this case, and calculate the correct *F*-values.

4.4—Check the calculations for obtaining the entries in the AOV given in Table 4.4.

4.5—Find the EMS for the mean squares for Within, *ABC* and *BC* in Table 4.4. If it is now possible, construct an approximate *F*-test of the hypothesis that the interaction *BC* is zero. If not, why not?

Reference

Bowles, Robert L. 1950. Accuracy of certain approximate methods in predicting the correct model for experiments with unequal frequencies in the subclasses. Unpublished M.S. thesis, Iowa State University, Ames.

CHAPTER 5

Extension of Exact and Approximate Methods to n-Way Classifications With Unequal and Disproportionate Subclass Numbers

5.1—Introduction. The methods discussed in the preceding chapters are all applicable to an n-way classification AOV, although the computations involved are considerably increased for each factor added.

Let an experiment have n factors—A at r levels, B at s levels, C at t levels, D at u levels, E at v levels, etc. The fixed model is:

$$
\begin{aligned}
Y_{ijklm\text{---}} &= \mu + \alpha_i + \beta_j + (\alpha\beta)_{ij} + \gamma_k + (\alpha\gamma)_{ik} \\
&+ (\beta\gamma)_{jk} + (\alpha\beta\gamma)_{ijk} + \delta_l + (\alpha\delta)_{il} + (\beta\delta)_{jl} \\
&+ (\alpha\beta\delta)_{ijl} + (\gamma\delta)_{kl} + (\alpha\gamma\delta)_{ikl} + (\beta\gamma\delta)_{jkl} \\
&+ (\alpha\beta\gamma\delta)_{ijkl} + \cdots + \epsilon_{ijklm\text{---}},
\end{aligned}
$$

where $i = 1, \ldots, r; j = 1, \ldots, s; k = 1, \ldots, t$; etc., and the

$$\epsilon_{ijklm\text{---}} \text{ are independently } \mathcal{N}(0, \sigma^2) .$$

5.2—Method of fitting constants. If it is known that no interaction is present in the population and an exact analysis is desired, then the method of fitting constants is available. This entails find ing first $R[a, b, c, d, \ldots]$, which is the SS for all main effects. One main effect is then deleted and the reduced model is fitted. In order to solve the least square equations, the usual additional model assumptions made are:

$$\sum_i \alpha_i = \sum_j \beta_j = \sum_i (\alpha\beta)_{ij} = \sum_j (\alpha\beta)_{ij} = \sum_k \gamma_k = \sum_i (\alpha\gamma)_{ik}$$

$$= \sum_k (\alpha\gamma)_{ik} = , \text{ etc. } = 0.$$

The difference between $R[a, b, c, d, \ldots]$ and the SS for the reduced model gives the SS for the deleted main effect. For example, deleting the main effect A will lead to $R[b, c, d, \ldots]$, and then $R[a] = R[a, b, c, d, \ldots] - R[b, c, d, \ldots]$. Each main effect SS can be calculated in this manner. As usual, Within SS = Total SS − Subclass SS, and the Within MS is the error term for the F-tests for this fixed effect model.

Table 5.1 gives a partial analysis of the n-way AOV.

TABLE 5.1
n-WAY AOV—FITTING CONSTANTS

Source	df	SS
Main effects $A, B,$ $C, D, \ldots$	$(r - 1) + (s - 1) + (t - 1) + \cdots$	$R[a, b, c, d, \ldots]$
$B, C, D, \ldots$ ignoring A	$(s - 1) + (t - 1) + (u - 1) + \cdots$	$R[b, c, d, \ldots]$
A eliminating $B, C, D, \ldots$	$(r - 1)$	$R[a] = R[a, b, c, d \ldots] - R[b, c, d, \ldots]$
$A, C, D, \ldots$ ignoring B	$(r - 1) + (t - 1) + (u - 1) + \cdots$	$R[a, c, d, \ldots]$
B eliminating $A, C, D, \ldots$ etc.	$(s - 1)$	$R[b] = R[a, b, c, d, \ldots] - R[a, c, d, \ldots]$

5.3—Method of weighted squares of means. If it is known that interaction is present in the population and an exact analysis is desired, then the method of weighted squares of means may be used to obtain SS's for the main effects. The definition of the SS's is extended quite easily to n factors. For example,

$$\text{SS}(A) = \sum_i N_i(y_{i\ldots} - c)^2, \text{ where}$$

(1) $y_{i\ldots}$ is the mean of all observations occurring in the ith level of A,

(2) $\dfrac{1}{N_i} = \dfrac{1}{s^2 t^2 u^2} \displaystyle\sum_{jklm} \dfrac{1}{n_{ijklm}}$, the summation being over all subscripts except i,

$$(3) \quad c = \frac{\sum_i \mathcal{N}_i y_{i\ldots} \underline{\hspace{1cm}}}{\sum_i \mathcal{N}_i} \cdot$$

All of the other main effect SS's are obtained in an analogous fashion. The Within MS is then the denominator for the *F*-tests on the main effects.

This method does not include a test as to which of the several interactions may be significantly different from zero. If an exact analysis, providing such a test, is desired, the general method of linear hypothesis theory presented earlier may be used in case the functions involved are estimable.

5.4—Preliminary test for interaction in the population. If it is not known whether interaction is significant or not, then a preliminary test can be made. $R[a, b, ab, c, ac, bc, abc, d, \ldots]$ is calculated as the Subclass SS. Then $R[a, b, c, d, \ldots]$, the reduction in sums of squares due to the main effects only, is obtained by solving the pertinent normal equations. (This is the first step in the method of fitting constants.) The SS for all of the interactions combined is given by the difference of these two, that is,

$$\text{Interaction SS} = \text{Subclass SS} - R[a, b, c, d, \ldots] \, .$$

The *df* for the pooled interactions is $(rstuv\text{———} - 1) - (r - 1) - (s - 1) - (t - 1) - \cdots$. If the *F*-test for interaction is nonsignificant, then the analysis is completed by the method of fitting constants. If the *F*-test is significant, the analysis is completed by the method of weighted squares of means. It should be realized that when the final method of analysis is conditional upon the result of a preliminary test, the probability level of final tests will be disturbed to some extent. To control the disturbance in the final tests, say, to insure that the final tests are at the .05 probability level, it is likely, in general, that the probability level of the preliminary test should be at the .25 probability level.

5.5—Method of unweighted means. The approximate analysis, using the method of unweighted means, reduces to an analysis of an *n*-way AOV with one observation per cell from which the SS's for main effects and interactions may be computed independently, since the addition theorem for the sums of squares holds in this case. The correction factor for the Within MS is

$$\frac{1}{\bar{n}_h} = \frac{1}{rstuv\text{------}} \sum_{ijklm\text{------}} \frac{1}{n_{ijklm\text{------}}}.$$

Thus, the Error MS for the experiment is $\dfrac{\text{Within MS}}{\bar{n}_h}$.

5.6—Method of expected subclass numbers. The approximate analysis, using the method of expected subclass numbers, proceeds as the usual analysis of a proportional n-way AOV, once the adjusted subclass frequencies and totals are obtained. In the case of the n-way classification,

$$E(n_{ijklm\text{------}}) = \frac{(n_{.jklm\text{------}})(n_{i.klm\text{------}})(n_{ij.lm\text{------}}) \cdots}{(n_{.....\text{------}})^{p-1}},$$

where p is the number of factors in the numerator. The χ^2 test to test the assumption required of this approximate analysis is

$$\chi^2 = \sum_{ijklm\text{------}} \frac{[n_{ijklm\text{------}} - E(n_{ijklm\text{------}})]^2}{E(n_{ijklm\text{------}})}$$

with $(r-1)(s-1)(t-1)(u-1) \ldots df.$

CHAPTER 6

Analysis of Covariance

6.1—Introduction. In introductory statistical methods courses the analysis of covariance was introduced primarily as a means to permit valid treatment comparisons using observations on one variate, say Y, after removing the effect of a possible disturbing second variate, say X. In this chapter, after reviewing the standard analysis of covariance techniques, we will extend them to the case of unequal numbers of observations in the subclasses and the case of two or more concomitant variates. We begin by calling attention to several additional uses in general of this important statistical tool. As R. A. Fisher (1946) said, ". . . covariance combines the advantages and reconciles the requirements of regression and analysis of variance."

6.2—Illustration of a covariance model for a two-way classification with a single observation in the subclasses. As a review we consider a fixed-effects model in which the rows are treatments and the columns blocks, that is,

$$Y_{ij} = \mu + \tau_i + \rho_j + \beta(X_{ij} - x_{..}) + \epsilon_{ij}, \qquad (6.1)$$

where Y_{ij} is the yield or response, τ_i is the treatment effect, ρ_j is the block effect, ϵ_{ij} is $\mathrm{NID}(0, \sigma^2)$, X_{ij} is a concomitant variate or covariate, Y_{ij} has a linear regression on X_{ij} with regression coefficient β, and $x_{..}$ is the overall sample mean of X_{ij}.

From the standpoint of the analysis of variance (6.1) may be written as

$$Y_{ij} - \beta(X_{ij} - x_{..}) = \mu + \tau_i + \rho_j + \epsilon_{ij}. \qquad (6.2)$$

In this form (6.2) is the typical model for the analysis of variance of the quantities

$$Y_{ij} - \beta(X_{ij} - x_{..}),$$

which are the deviations of Y_{ij} from its linear regression on X_{ij}, or the values of Y_{ij} after adjustment for this linear regression. In this setting τ_i may be regarded as the population effect of the ith treatment on Y_{ij}, after adjustment for the linear regression on the covariate X_{ij}. Hence, the technique enables us to remove that part of an observed treatment effect which can be attributed to a linear association with X_{ij}.

6.3—Principal uses of covariance.

(1) To increase precision in randomized experiments (usual use).

If σ_y^2 is the population experimental error variance when covariance is not employed, the adjustments by covariance reduce this variance to a value which is effectively approximated by

$$\sigma_y^2(1 - \rho^2) \left\{ 1 + \frac{1}{f_e - 2} \right\}, \tag{6.3}$$

where ρ is the population correlation coefficient of Y_{ij} and X_{ij} and f_e is the error degrees of freedom. If $\rho < .3$, the reduction in variance is inconsequential, but as ρ increases towards unity, sizable increases in precision are obtained.

(2) To remove the effects of disturbing variables in analytical studies of observation data.

In fields of research in which randomized experiments are not feasible, we may compare the means on the same characteristic for two or more groups after adjusting by covariance for a second characteristic. This covariance adjustment for the second characteristic may result in a more sensitive comparison for the first characteristic of the groups.

(3) To provide additional information on the nature of treatment effects.

If the treatment differences in Y disappear after adjusting by linear covariance for X, this suggests that the treatment differences in the unadjusted Y's may be simply a reflection of the differences produced by the treatments on X.

(4) To fit regressions in multiple classifications.

After fitting a separate regression of Y on X within each class, we may test whether the slopes of the lines differ from class to class; and, if advisable, make a combined estimate of the common slope.

(5) To analyze data when some observations are missing.

Covariance may be used to provide an alternative technique for analysis in missing value situations. To each missing observation assign any convenient value (for example, 0, 5, or 100) and introduce a dummy X-variate that takes the value 1 for the missing unit, and 0 for all other units. The standard covariance computations then give the correct least squares estimates of the treatment means and the exact F-test. This method is probably slower than the use of available missing value formulas, but it is useful with classifications for which missing value formulas have not been worked out, and where exact F-tests are important since the formula method provides approximate F-tests.

6.4—Standard covariance computations for a randomized block design.

SV	df	Σx^2	Σxy	Σy^2	Deviations From Regression		
					df	SS	MS
Treatments	$t-1$	T_{xx}	T_{xy}	T_{yy}			
Error	f_e	E_{xx}	E_{xy}	E_{yy}	$f_e - 1$	$E_{yy} - \dfrac{E_{xy}^2}{E_{xx}}$	S_e^2
Sum	$t-1+f_e$	S_{xx}	S_{xy}	S_{yy}	$t+f_e-2$	$S_{yy} - \dfrac{S_{xy}^2}{S_{xx}}$	
Adjusted Treatment Means					$t-1$	$T_{yy} - \dfrac{S_{xy}^2}{S_{xx}} + \dfrac{E_{xy}^2}{E_{xx}}$	S_t^2

The F-test for comparing adjusted treatment means is effected by comparing the calculated $F = S_t^2/S_e^2$ with the corresponding tabular F with $t-1$ and $f_e - 1$ degrees of freedom.

The adjusted treatment means may be obtained from the formula

$$\hat{y}_{i.} = y_{i.} - b_{xy}(x_{i.} - x_{..}),\qquad (6.4)$$

where

$$b_{xy} = \frac{E_{xy}}{E_{xx}}. \qquad (6.5)$$

Example 6.1—Snedecor and Cochran (1967) give an example of the analysis of the yield (Y) adjusted for stand (X) of 6 varieties of corn in a

randomized complete block experiment. The yield is in terms of pounds of
field weight of ear corn and the stand is measured by the number of stalks.

TABLE 6.1

NUMBER OF STALKS PER PLOT, AND YIELDS (FIELD WEIGHT IN POUNDS OF EAR
CORN), IN A RANDOMIZED BLOCKS EXPERIMENT

	Block									
	1		2		3		4		Total	
Variety	X	Y	X	Y	X	Y	X	Y	X	Y
A	28	202	22	165	27	191	19	134	96	692
B	23	145	26	201	28	203	24	180	101	729
C	27	188	24	185	27	185	28	220	106	778
D	24	201	28	231	30	238	30	261	112	931
E	30	202	26	178	26	198	29	226	111	804
F	30	228	25	221	27	207	24	204	106	860
Total	162	1166	151	1181	165	1222	154	1225	632	4794

					Deviations From Regression		
Source	df	Σx^2	Σxy	Σy^2	df	SS	MS
Blocks	3	21.67	8.50	436.17			
Varieties (V)	5	45.83	559.25	9490.00			
Error (E)	15	113.83	917.25	8752.33	14	1361.07	97.22
$V + E$	20	159.66	1476.50	18242.33	19	4587.99	
Adjusted Treatment Means					5	3226.92	645.38

We compare

$$\text{calculated } F = \frac{645.38}{97.22} = 6.64$$

with

$$\text{tabular } F_{.01}(5, 14) = 4.69$$

and have evidence that the hypothesis of equal adjusted variety mean

$$H_0: \mu_{1adj.} = \mu_{2adj.} = \mu_{3adj.} = \mu_{4adj.} = \mu_{5adj.} = \mu_{6adj.}$$

is false. Using (6.5) we find

$$b_{xy} = \frac{917.25}{113.83} = 8.058 ,$$

and using (6.4) we may find the adjusted variety means. For example

$$\hat{y}_{1.} = \bar{y}_{1.} - b_{xy}(x_{1.} - x_{..})$$
$$= 173 - 8.058(24.0 - 26.33)$$
$$= 191.8 .$$

The unadjusted and adjusted variety means are computed as

TABLE 6.2

UNADJUSTED AND ADJUSTED VARIETY MEANS

	V_A	V_B	V_C	V_D	V_E	V_F
Unadjusted means ($\bar{y}_{i.}$)	173.00	182.25	194.50	232.75	201.00	215.00
Adjusted means ($\hat{y}_{i.}$)	191.8	191.0	193.1	219.3	189.6	213.6

The problem of multiple comparisons for the adjusted means will be considered in a separate chapter with other multiple comparison situations.

6.5—Analysis of covariance for a two-factor experiment in randomized blocks with a single observation per treatment combination. The fixed-effects model (6.1) becomes

$$Y_{ijk} = \mu + \rho_i + \alpha_j + \beta_k + (\alpha\beta)_{jk} + \beta(X_{ijk} - x_{...}) + \epsilon_{ijk}, \quad (6.6)$$

where Y_{ijk} is the response, μ is the overall population mean of the Y's, ρ_i is the block effect, α_j is the first factor effect, β_k is the second factor effect, $(\alpha\beta)_{jk}$ is the interaction effect, ϵ_{ijk} is $NID(0, \sigma^2)$, X_{ijk} is a concomitant variate, Y_{ijk} has a linear regression on X_{ijk} with regression coefficient β, and $x_{...}$ is the overall sample mean of X_{ijk}.

Example 6.2—The data in Table 6.3 given by Wishart (1938) include initial weights and growth rates of 30 pigs classified according to pen, sex, and type of ration. The pens are assumed to play the role of block effect, hence the observations are assumed represented by model (6.6).

TABLE 6.3

INITIAL WEIGHT IN POUNDS AND GROWTH RATE IN POUNDS
PER WEEK OF PIGS IN A TWO-FACTOR EXPERIMENT
IN RANDOMIZED BLOCKS

Pen	Treat-ment	Sex	Initial Weight (w)	Growth Rate in Pounds per Week (g)
I	A	F	48	9.94
	B	F	48	10.00
	C	F	48	9.75
	C	M	48	9.11
	B	M	39	8.51
	A	M	38	9.52
II	B	F	32	9.24
	C	F	28	8.66
	A	F	32	9.48
	C	M	37	8.50
	A	M	35	8.21
	B	M	38	9.95
III	C	F	33	7.63
	A	F	35	9.32
	B	F	41	9.34
	B	M	46	8.43
	C	M	42	8.90
	A	M	41	9.32
IV	C	F	50	10.37
	A	M	48	10.56
	B	F	46	9.68
	A	F	46	10.98
	B	M	40	8.86
	C	M	42	9.51
V	B	F	37	9.67
	A	F	32	8.82
	C	F	30	8.57
	B	M	40	9.20
	C	M	40	8.76
	A	M	43	10.42

TABLE 6.3 (continued)

Source	df	Σw^2	Σwg	Σg^2	df	SS	MS
					for Deviations From Regression		

Source	df	Σw^2	Σwg	Σg^2	df	SS	MS
Total	29	1108.70	78.979	16.6068			
Pen	4	605.87	40.324	4.9607			
Ration (R)	2	5.40	−0.171	2.3242			
Sex (S)	1	32.03	−3.813	0.4538			
RS	2	22.47	3.099	0.4642			
Error (E)	20	442.93	39.540	8.4039	19	4.8742	0.2565
$R + E$	22	448.33	39.369	10.7281	21	7.2710	
Adjusted Ration Means					2	2.3968	1.1984

We compare

$$\text{calculated } F = \frac{1.1984}{0.2565} = 4.67$$

with

$$\text{tabular } F_{.05}(2,\ 19) = 3.52$$

and have evidence at the 5% point that the hypothesis of equal adjusted population ration means is false. Using (6.5) we find

$$b_{wg} = \frac{39.540}{442.93} = 0.089269 \,,$$

and using (6.4) suitably modified we may find the adjusted ration means. For example,

$$\hat{g}_{A..} = \bar{g}_{A..} - b_{wg}(w_{A..} - w_{...})$$
$$= 9.657 - (0.089269)(39.8 - 40.1)$$
$$= 9.684 \,.$$

To test for rations without adjustment for initial weight we obtain from the values in the above table

$$\text{calculated } F = \frac{2.3242/2}{8.4039/20} = 2.76 \,,$$

which is not significant at the 5% level. In a similar manner we may test the sex and interaction effects adjusted for initial weight. In a later chapter we will consider the problem of multiple comparisons of the adjusted means for the above case.

6.6—Covariance analysis of multiple classification tables with unequal subclass numbers. In this section we will extend

the methods discussed earlier to the situation represented by Hazel's (1946) data given in Table 6.4.

TABLE 6.4

NUMBERS, WEIGHTS, AGES, AND INBREEDING OF LAMES CLASSED ACCORDING TO AGE OF DAM AND TYPE OF BIRTH

Type of Birth	Attribute		Age of Dam		
			Mature dams P_1	Young dams P_2	Total
Single lambs (T_1)	Number		179	105	284
	Weight	(pounds) Y	15187	7740	22927
	Age	(days) A	21392	12639	34031
	Inbreeding	(per cent) P	1768.9	1376.9	3145.8
Twin lambs (T_2)	Number		117	18	135
	Weight	(pounds) Y	8422	1138	9560
	Age	(days) A	14141	2150	16291
	Inbreeding	(per cent) P	1098.8	72.4	1171.2
Twin lambs reared singly (T_3)	Number		56	3	59
	Weight	(pounds) Y	4346	213	4559
	Age	(days) A	6716	366	7082
	Inbreeding	(per cent) P	634.6	66.2	700.8
Total	Number		352	126	478
	Weight	(pounds) Y	27955	9091	37046
	Age	(days) A	42249	15155	57404
	Inbreeding	(per cent) P	3502.3	1515.5	5017.8

$$\begin{aligned} S(Y^2) &= 2{,}963{,}362\,. & S(YA) &= 4{,}452{,}731\,. \\ S(A^2) &= 6{,}904{,}328\,. & S(YP) &= 378{,}947.0\,. \\ S(P^2) &= 92{,}156.64\,. & S(AP) &= 602{,}971.6\,. \end{aligned}$$

The notation and analysis for the data in Table 6.4 will be that given by Hazel (1946). The fixed effects model specification is

$$Y = a + d_1 D_1 + d_2 D_2 + t_1 T_1 + t_2 T_2 + t_3 T_3 \\ + b_a A + b_p P + E\,, \quad (6.7)$$

where the lower case letters represent the constants to be fitted and the capital letters are defined as follows: D_1 and D_2 take the values 1 and 0 or 0 and 1, depending upon whether an observation lies in the mature dam group or in the young dam group; T_1, T_2, and T_3 take the values 1, 0, and 0 or 0, 1, and 0 or 0, 0, and 1, depending upon where an observation lies with respect to type of birth; A and P are the values for age and per cent inbreeding which are associated with the particular observations, while E represents the error,

E is assumed independently $\mathcal{N}(0,\,\sigma^2)$ in order to make use of standard inference procedures based on normal distribution theory.

The least squares equations are:

(1) $478a +\ \ 352d_1 +\ \ 126d_2 +\ \ 284t_1 +\ \ 135t_2 +\ \ 59t_3 +\ \ 57404b_a +\ \ 5017.8b_p = 37046$

(2) $352a +\ \ 352d_1 +\ \ 0d_2 +\ \ 179t_1 +\ \ 117t_2 +\ \ 56t_3 +\ \ 42249b_a +\ \ 3502.3b_p = 27955$

(3) $126a +\ \ 0d_1 +\ \ 126d_2 +\ \ 105t_1 +\ \ 18t_2 +\ \ 3t_3 +\ \ 15155b_a +\ \ 1515.5b_p = 9091$

(4) $284a +\ \ 179d_1 +\ \ 105d_2 +\ \ 284t_1 +\ \ 0t_2 +\ \ 0t_3 +\ \ 34031b_a +\ \ 3145.8b_p = 22927$

(5) $135a +\ \ 117d_1 +\ \ 18d_2 +\ \ 0t_1 +\ \ 135t_2 +\ \ 0t_3 +\ \ 16291b_a +\ \ 1171.2b_p = 9560$

(6) $59a +\ \ 56d_1 +\ \ 3d_2 +\ \ 0t_1 +\ \ 0t_2 +\ \ 59t_3 +\ \ 7082b_a +\ \ 700.8b_p = 4559$

(7) $57404a +\ 42249d_1 +\ 15155d_2 +\ 34031t_1 +\ 16291t_2 +\ 7082t_3 +\ 6904328b_a +\ 602971.6b_p = 4452731$

(8) $5017.8a +\ 3502.3d_1 +\ 1515.5d_2 +\ 3145.8t_1 +\ 1171.2t_2 +\ 700.8t_3 +\ 602971.6b_a +\ 92156.64b_p = 378947.0$

By successive elimination the above equations may be reduced to

(2a) $83.821d_1 - 83.821d_2 = 859.379$

(3a) $-83.821d_1 + 83.821d_2 = -859.379$

(4a) $104.550t_1 - 73.281t_2 - 31.269t_3 = 1189.722$

(5a) $-73.281t_1 + 91.737t_2 - 18.456t_3 = -1108.822$

(6a) $-31.269t_1 - 18.456t_2 + 49.725t_3 = -80.900$

(7a) $10472.218b_a = 5130.711$

(8a) $38498.842b_p = -10639.150$.

It is evident that the above equations are not independent, since (2a) and (3a) sum to zero as do (4a), (5a), and (6a). In such case, we assume $d_1 + d_2 = 0$ and $t_1 + t_2 + t_3 = 0$ and replace, say, (2a) by the first and, say, (4a) by the second. With these assumptions, we find the following estimates:

$$\hat{d}_1 = 5.12628 \qquad \hat{t}_3 = 0.06773$$
$$\hat{d}_2 = -5.12628 \qquad \hat{b}_a = 0.48994$$
$$\hat{t}_1 = 6.67416 \qquad \hat{b}_p = -0.27635$$
$$\hat{t}_2 = -6.74192 \ .$$

We may now substitute these estimates in Equation (1) above to obtain $\hat{a} = 17.07158$.

Now, the total sum of squares of deviations from the general mean is

$$2,963,362 - \frac{(37,046)^2}{478} = 92,219.5 \ .$$

The reduction in sum of squares due to fitting all constants is, as usual, given by:

$$\hat{a}SY + \hat{d}_1SD_1Y + \hat{d}_2SD_2Y + \hat{t}_1ST_1Y + \hat{t}_2ST_2Y + \hat{t}_3ST_3Y + \hat{b}_aSAY$$
$$+ \hat{b}_pSPY - \frac{(SY)^2}{N} = 17.07158(37,046) + 5.12628(27,955)$$
$$+ \cdots - 0.27635(378,947.0) - \frac{(37,046)^2}{478} = 23,716.9 .$$

Further, it can be shown that the reduction in sum of squares of deviations due to fitting the levels of any one variable may be obtained by multiplying the particular estimates by the corresponding right hand sides of equations (2a) through (8a) as follows:

Age of dam SS $= (5.12628)(859.379)$
$\qquad\qquad\qquad\quad + (-5.12628)(-859.379) \quad = \quad 8810.8$
Type of birth SS $= (6.67416)(1189.722)$
$\qquad\qquad\qquad\quad + (-6.74192)(-1108.822)$
$\qquad\qquad\qquad\quad + (0.06776)(-80.900) \qquad = \quad 15410.5$
$\qquad$ Age SS $= (0.48994)(5130.711) \qquad\qquad = \quad 2513.7$
Per cent inbreeding SS $= (-0.27635)(-10,639.150) \; = \quad 2940.1$
Total of additional reduction in a sum of squares due
$\quad$ to fitting all constants for each level $\qquad\qquad\qquad = \; 29675.1 .$

We may now construct the following AOV as given in Table 6.5.

TABLE 6.5

ANALYSIS OF VARIANCE FOR WEIGHTS OF LAMBS

Source of Variation	df	SS	MS
Total	477	92219.5	
Due to fitting all constants	5	23716.9	
Error	472	68502.6	145.1
Several effects			
Age of dam	1	8810.8	8810.8 **
Type of birth	2	15410.5	7705.2 **
Age	1	2513.7	2513.7 **
Inbreeding	1	2940.1	2940.1 **

We may now calculate F-tests using the Error MS in the denominator and the respective effect MS as numerator. All effects are highly significant.

Problems

6.1—Using the data given in Table 6.1, check the entries in the analysis of covariance table also given in Table 6.1.

6.2—Using the information given in Table 6.1, construct an analysis of variance and a test for varieties using yield (Y). Now use this result and the result of the analysis of covariance to obtain additional information, if possible, on the nature of treatment effects.

6.3—Using the data given in Table 6.3, check the entries in the analysis of covariance given in Table 6.3.

6.4—Check the calculations for obtaining the entries in Table 6.5.

6.5—Consult the reference Hazel (1946). Explain and comment on Hazel's investigation of the appropriateness of the model specification and analysis.

6.6—As stated in (5) of Section 6.3, covariance may be used to provide an alternative technique for analysis in missing value situations. Given the randomized blocks experiment below with one missing value, use the analysis of covariance to obtain a test for treatments.

	T_1	T_2	T_3	T_4
B_1	2	3	4	. . .
B_2	4	5	3	3
Total	6	8	7	3

The entry in $B_1 T_4$ is missing. Let the above observations correspond to the Y-values in a covariance table and assign 0 to all X-values except the missing value. Assign 1 to the X-value corresponding to the missing value and 0 to the Y missing value. From the above analysis obtain a proper substitute for the missing value.

6.7—Check the results of Problem 6.6 by the alternative methods of (1) formula, and (2) fitting constants.

6.8—A. The depth of fat on a pig is a useful measure of carcass quality. Three different breeding groups (lines) were studied to determine how much they differed in fat depth. Two pigs from each line were raised in the same pen. Six pens were used. The experimental arrangement was that of a randomized block with three treatments (lines) and six blocks (pens) and two observations for each treatment in each block.

The fat was measured when the animals were five months old. The animals were weighed at the same time. Fat and

weight are highly correlated. Pigs are marketed at a constant weight, therefore, the question of interest is whether
the lines differ in fat after adjusting for differences in
weight.

(1) Write the model and set out the analysis of covariance
in accordance with the experimental design. The line
totals and corrected sums of squares and products are
given below.

Totals	Wt.	Fat	n
Line A	2115	15.7	12
Line B	2439	16.1	12
Line C	2159	15.2	12

Corrected sums of squares and products.

	Wt.	Wt. × Fat	Fat
Total	17207	134.8	2.52
Pens	2425	38.0	0.77
Lines	5148	10.0	0.04
Pens × lines	4309	42.5	0.75
Pigs within pen × line	5325	44.3	0.96

(2) Make an F-test for line differences in adjusted fat
means.
(3) Give the adjusted line means correct to two decimal
places.

B. (1) How much is gained in precision by adjusting for a
covariate in the above example?
(2) The purpose of using covariance in the example was
to increase precision and remove the effect of a disturbing variable. What other uses does the analysis of
covariance have as a statistical method?
(3) An experimenter wishes to measure treatment effects
on gain in weight of animals over a specific period. He
knows initial weight influences the gains and wants to
adjust for it. He analyzes the differences between the
initial and final weights instead of using the initial
weights as covariates. What can be said for and against
this approach?

C. Instead of making the usual calculations for the treatment
sum of squares in the analysis of covariance, one can use an

approximation by taking the sum of squares of deviations of adjusted treatment means.

(1) Show how the approximation differs from the usual calculation for the adjusted treatment sum of squares. *Hint:* Using the usual covariance notation, show that the sum of squares of deviations of adjusted treatment means would be:

$$T_{yyA} = \Sigma[(y_i. - y..) - b(x_i. - x..)]^2$$
$$= T_{yy} - 2bT_{xy} + b^2T_{xy}.$$

Also, show that the sum of squares for adjusted treatment differences in the usual covariance analysis would be:

$$T_{yyR} = T_{yy} - \frac{(T_{xy} + E_{xy})^2}{T_{xx} + E_{xx}} + \frac{(E_{xy})^2}{E_{xx}}$$

Let $b_T = T_{xy}/T_{xx'}$ $b = E_{xy}/E_{xx'}$ then find
$$T_{yyR} - T_{yyA}.$$

(2) What will be the effect on the F-test for treatments?
(3) What does the approximate method ignore?
(4) When can the approximate method be useful?

References

Anderson, R. L., and T. A. Bancroft. 1952. *Statistical Theory in Research.* McGraw-Hill, Inc., New York.

Das, M. N. 1953. Analysis of covariance in two-way classification with disproportionate cell frequencies. *Journal of Indian Society of Agricultural Statistics* 5:161–178.

DeLury, D. B. 1948. The analysis of covariance. *Biometrics* 4:153–170.

Fisher, R. A. 1946. *Statistical Methods for Research Workers,* 10th ed. Oliver and Boyd, Ltd., Edinburgh.

Hazel, L. N. 1946. The covariance analysis of multiple classification tables with unequal subclass numbers. *Biometrics* 2:21–25.

Johnson, P. O., and Fei Tsao. 1945. Factorial design and covariance in the study of individual educational development. *Psychometrika* 10:133–162.

Snedecor, George W., and William G. Cochran. 1967. *Statistical Methods.* Iowa State University Press, Ames.

Special Issue on the Analysis of Covariance, *Biometrics,* Vol. 13, No. 3, 1957.

Wilks, S. S. 1938. The analysis of variance and covariance in non-orthogonal data. *Metron* 13:141–154.

Wishart, J. 1936. Tests of significance in analysis of covariance. *Journal of the Royal Statistical Society, Supplements* 3:79–82.

———. 1938. Growth-rate determinations in nutrition studies with the bacon pig and their analysis. *Biometrika* 30:16–28.

CHAPTER 7

Orthogonal Polynomials

7.1—Use of orthogonal polynomials. The usual method of orthogonal polynomials is an application of the technique of multiple regression to fitting a polynomial by least squares when the independent variable is equally spaced. Such methods are available for unequally spaced X values but difficult to apply and will not be given here (see Kendall and Stuart, 1958; and Cox, 1958). This use of orthogonal polynomials has some very desirable advantages over the straightforward regression methods of fitting polynomials. First of all, the computing time for curve fitting using orthogonal polynomials is less, particularly if a polynomial of third degree or higher is fitted. Secondly, the orthogonal polynomials are so constructed that any term of the polynomial is independent of any other term. For a proper model specification this property of independence allows the fitting to be done in successive stages, the usefulness of fitting terms of higher and higher degree being observed and tested for significance at each stage. In other words, each regression coefficient is computed independently of the others.

In the following discussion the values of X, the independent variable, are assumed to be 1, 2, 3, . . . , n. If the independent variable of a particular problem does not have equally spaced intervals equal to one, each X value is divided by d, where d is the difference between any two adjacent values of X. If the smallest value of X is then not equal to one, the X data are further coded by adding or subtracting a constant in order to obtain X values of 1, 2, 3, . . . , n.

7.2—The usual model assumed when using orthogonal polynomials. Given an independent variable X which assumes values 1, 2, 3, . . . , n and a single dependent Y value[1] for each X value, the general polynomial model is

$$Y = \alpha_0 + \alpha_1 X + \alpha_2 X^2 + \alpha_3 X^3 + \cdots + \alpha_j X^j \\ + \cdots + \alpha_k X^k + \epsilon, \quad (7.1)$$

where $\epsilon \sim \mathrm{NID}(0, \sigma^2)$. Equation (7.1) may be replaced by

$$Y = A_0 + A_1 \xi_1' + A_2 \xi_2' + A_3 \xi_3' + \cdots + A_j \xi_j' \\ + \cdots + A_k \xi_k' + \epsilon, \quad (7.2)$$

where $\epsilon \sim \mathrm{NID}(0, \sigma^2)$, or

$$\hat{Y} = A_0' + A_1' \xi_1' + A_2' \xi_2' + A_3' \xi_3' + \cdots + A_j' \xi_j' \\ + \cdots + A_k' \xi_k', \quad (7.2\text{a})$$

where the A_j''s are estimates of the A_j's. Also

$$\xi_1' = \lambda_1 \xi_1 = \lambda_1 (X - \bar{X})$$
$$\xi_2' = \lambda_2 \xi_2 = \lambda_2 \left[(X - \bar{X})^2 - \frac{n^2 - 1}{12} \right] \quad (7.3)$$
$$\xi_3' = \lambda_3 \xi_3 = \lambda_3 \left[(X - \bar{X})^3 - \frac{(X - \bar{X})(3n^2 - 7)}{20} \right], \text{ etc.}$$

In general,

$$\xi_{r+1}' = \lambda_{r+1} \xi_{r+1}$$
$$\xi_{r+1} = \xi_1 \xi_r - \frac{r^2(n^2 - r^2)}{4(4r^2 - 1)} \xi_{r-1}. \quad (7.4)$$

Also $\bar{X}$ is the mean value of X, and since X assumes values 1, 2, . . . , n,

$$\bar{X} = \frac{1}{n} \sum_{i=1}^{n} i = \frac{n + 1}{2}.$$

The λ_i's, which are functions of n, are chosen such that the values of ξ_i''s are integers reduced to lowest terms. For example, if X takes the values 1, 2, 3, then $\bar{X} = 2$. If it is desired to calculate λ_2, then by (7.3)

---

[1] Note that it will be shown later how the procedures developed here may be adjusted for use when there are more values than one for Y (but an *equal number*) for each X value.

$$\xi_2' \text{ (for } X = 1) = \lambda_2[(-1)^2 - \tfrac{2}{3}] = \frac{\lambda_2}{3}$$

$$\xi_2' \text{ (for } X = 2) = \lambda_2[(0)^2 - \tfrac{2}{3}] = \frac{-2}{3}\lambda_2$$

$$\xi_2' \text{ (for } X = 3) = \lambda_2[(1)^2 - \tfrac{2}{3}] = \frac{\lambda_2}{3}.$$

Hence $\lambda_2 = 3$, so that the corresponding values of ξ_2' are 1, -2, and 1. If tables of orthogonal polynomial values are available, it is not necessary to compute the λ_i's, since they will be tabulated.

From the definition of the ξ_i''s, it follows that

$$\sum_{j=1}^{n} {}'_{ij} = 0, \quad \Sigma\xi_i'\xi_j' = 0 \quad \text{for} \quad i \neq j. \tag{7.5}$$

Since $\xi_i' = \lambda\xi_i$, then (7.5) yields:

$$\sum_{j=1}^{n} \xi_{ij} = 0 \quad \text{and} \quad \Sigma\xi_i\xi_j = 0 \quad \text{for} \quad i \neq j. \tag{7.5a}$$

7.3—Formulas for estimating A_j coefficients. Using the method of least squares to obtain the estimates for the coefficients in Equation (7.2) we minimize Q with respect to A_j', where

$$Q = \Sigma(Y - A_0' - A_1'\xi_1 - A_2'\xi_2 - \cdots - A_j'\xi_j - \cdots - A_k'\xi_k)^2.$$

The normal equations, obtained by setting the partial derivatives

$$\frac{\partial Q}{\partial A_0'}, \quad \frac{\partial Q}{\partial A_1'}, \quad \cdots, \quad \frac{\partial Q}{\partial A_k'},$$

equal to zero, are:

$$\begin{aligned}
\Sigma Y &= \Sigma A_0' + \Sigma A_1'\xi_1' + \Sigma A_2'\xi_2' + \cdots + \Sigma A_k'\xi_k' \\
\Sigma\xi_1'Y &= \Sigma A_0'\xi_1' + \Sigma A_1'\xi_1'^2 + \Sigma A_2'\xi_1'\xi_2' + \cdots + \Sigma A_k'\xi_1'\xi_k' \\
&\vdots \qquad\quad \vdots \qquad\quad \vdots \\
\Sigma\xi_k'Y &= \Sigma A_0'\xi_k' + \Sigma A_1'\xi_1'\xi_k' + \Sigma A_2'\xi_2'\xi_k' + \cdots + \Sigma A_k'\xi_k'^2.
\end{aligned} \tag{7.6}$$

Making use of conditions (7.5) in (7.6) we obtain the following $(k + 1)$ equations in $(k + 1)$ unknowns:

$$\begin{aligned}
\Sigma Y &= nA_0' \\
\Sigma\xi_1'Y &= \Sigma A_1'\xi_1'^2 \\
\Sigma\xi_2'Y &= \Sigma A_2'\xi_2'^2 \\
&\vdots \qquad\quad \vdots \\
\Sigma\xi_k'Y &= \Sigma A_k'\xi_k'^2.
\end{aligned} \tag{7.7}$$

From (7.7) we obtain

$$A_0' = \frac{\Sigma Y}{n} = \bar{Y}, \quad A_j' = \frac{\Sigma \xi_j' Y}{\Sigma \xi_j'^2}. \tag{7.8}$$

The respective reduction in sums of squares are:

$$A_0' \Sigma Y, \quad A_j' \Sigma \xi_j' Y. \tag{7.9}$$

Tables of orthogonal polynomial values are available in which the ξ_i''s and $\Sigma \xi_j'^2$ are tabulated. The tables by Fisher and Yates give values through $n = 52$ observations, and Anderson and Houseman (1963) have extended these tables through $n = 104$ observations. Thus, the only quantities requiring calculation directly to evaluate (7.8) are $\Sigma \xi_i' Y$ and ΣY.

7.4—Analysis of variance for polynomial regression using orthogonal polynomials. If each X has only one associated Y value, then the experimental error variance, σ^2, must be estimated by the sample residual mean square. In such case, if it is known a priori, say, theoretically or from past experience with similar data, that the data are properly fitted by a kth degree polynomial where $k < n$, then the mean square deviation from the kth degree regression may be used to estimate σ^2. This estimate of σ^2 may be used, then, as the denominator for all F-values calculated to test the significance of the reduction in sums of squares due to fitting the linear, quadratic, cubic, etc. up to and including the kth degree term.

Some writers have recommended a testing procedure carried out in successive steps using the corresponding mean square deviation as the estimate of σ^2 to test the significance of the reduction in sums of squares due to any particular degree term. For example, the linear component is tested for significance with the F-test,

$$F_1 = \frac{\text{MS (linear regression)}}{\text{MS (deviation from linear regression)}}.$$

If F_1 is significant, the quadratic component is then tested in a similar manner, etc. Those who advocate this procedure usually suggest investigating one further power after the first nonsignificant power appears. This particular stepwise procedure does not, in general, provide an exact test for each power component, since the denominators are overestimates of σ^2, that is, they contain estimates of reduction in sums of squares due to any subsequent power terms that should be in the proper model. It is sometimes argued that the above stepwise testing procedure is on the *safe* side since if F_i is significant, then the value of F using an appropriate estimate of σ^2 will also be significant. However, such a procedure will not be sensitive in declaring as significant all terms that should be so declared.

The procedure described in the first paragraph of this section or an alternative one in the case of more than one value of Y for each X (to be described later) would appear to be the preferred methods.

Example 7.1—The data in Table 7.1 give the relationship between $ph(X)$ and activity of the enzyme asparaginare (Y). The columnar values ξ'_1, ξ'_2, ξ'_3, ξ'_4, and ξ'_5 are obtained from the tables of orthogonal polynomial values under $n = 14$. Only seven values are given in the tables, the values corresponding to the latter half of the Y values. If j is even, the values under the column ξ'_j are symmetric, as exemplified by the columns ξ'_2 and ξ'_4. If j is odd, the values under the column ξ'_j are symmetric but of opposite sign, as exemplified by the columns ξ'_1, ξ'_3, and ξ'_5. Thus, it is necessary for the tables to show only half of the coefficients for each columnar ξ'_j. The tables also contain the values of $\Sigma \xi'^2_j$ and λ_j. The values of $\Sigma \xi'_j Y_i$ can be calculated by accumulative multiplication, although for illustrative purposes each individual multiplication is shown in Table 7.1.

TABLE 7.1

Data and Calculations for Example 7.1

X	Y	ξ'_1	ξ'_2	ξ'_3	ξ'_4	ξ'_5	$\xi'_1 Y$	$\xi'_2 Y$	$\xi'_3 Y$	$\xi'_4 Y$	$\xi'_5 Y$
1	0.2	−13	13	−143	143	−143	−2.6	2.6	−28.6	28.6	−28.6
2	0.4	−11	7	−11	−77	187	−4.4	2.8	−4.4	−30.8	74.8
3	1.4	−9	2	66	−132	132	−12.6	2.8	92.4	−184.8	184.8
4	4.1	−7	−2	98	−92	−28	−28.7	−8.2	401.8	−377.2	−114.8
5	6.6	−5	−5	95	−13	−139	−33.0	−33.0	627.0	−85.8	−917.4
6	8.7	−3	−7	67	63	−145	−26.1	−60.9	582.9	548.1	−1261.5
7	9.8	−1	−8	24	108	−60	−9.8	−78.4	235.2	1058.4	−588.0
8	9.9	1	−8	−24	108	60	9.9	−79.2	−237.6	1069.2	594.0
9	9.5	3	−7	−67	63	145	28.5	−66.5	−636.5	598.5	1377.5
10	8.2	5	−5	−95	−13	139	41.0	−41.0	−779.0	−106.6	1139.8
11	6.4	7	−2	−98	−92	28	44.8	−12.8	−627.2	−588.8	179.2
12	3.3	9	2	−66	−132	−132	29.7	6.6	−217.8	−435.6	−435.6
13	0.3	11	7	11	−77	−187	3.3	2.1	3.3	−23.1	−56.1
14	0.1	13	13	143	143	143	1.3	1.3	14.3	14.3	14.3
105	68.9						41.3	−361.8	−574.2	1484.4	162.4
						$\Sigma \xi'^2$	910	728	97240	136136	235144
						λ_j	2	$\frac{1}{2}$	$\frac{5}{6}$	$\frac{7}{12}$	$\frac{7}{80}$

Using (7.8)

$$A_0' = \bar{Y} = 4.9214$$

$$A_1' = \frac{41.3}{910} = 0.045385$$

$$A_2' = \frac{-361.8}{728} = -0.49698$$

$$A_3' = \frac{-574.2}{97240} = -0.0059050$$

$$A_4' = \frac{1484.4}{136136} = 0.010904$$

$$A_5' = \frac{162.4}{235144} = 0.00069064 .$$

Then the AOV in Table 7.2 is obtained.

TABLE 7.2

AOV FOR EXAMPLE 7.1

Source	df	SS	MS	F
Linear regr.	1	1.8744	1.8744	11.95**
Quadratic regr.	1	179.8060	179.8060	1146.72**
Cubic regr.	1	3.3906	3.3906	21.62**
Quartic regr.	1	16.1856	16.1856	103.22**
Quintic regr.	1	0.1122	0.1122	<1
Dev. from quintic regr.	8	1.2548	0.1568	
Total	13	202.6236		

Implicit in the F-tests of Table 7.2 is the assumption that some prior knowledge motivated the experimenter to expect a regression equation of the fifth degree, since the estimate of σ^2 for all F-tests is taken as MS (deviation from fifth-degree regression). However, since the fifth-degree regression is nonsignificant, he may decide not to use it in the regression equation and thus use MS (deviation from fourth-degree regression) as his estimate of σ^2 for the experiment. In using this latter procedure the experimenter is essentially making use of inference based on an incompletely specified model, that is, he is pooling two mean squares after a preliminary test of significance. Analysis of incompletely specified models for linear multiple regression, given in the two references by Larson and Bancroft (1963), may be directly applied to the case of polynomial regression.

Table 7.3 shows the AOV if the questionable stepwise testing procedure is used, that is, testing one power at a time, each one with a different denominator in the F-test. Note that linear regression is not significant in Table 7.3 although it is highly significant in Table 7.2.

TABLE 7.3

ALTERNATE AOV FOR EXAMPLE 7.1

Source	df	SS	MS	F
Total	13	202.6236		
Linear regr.	1	1.8744	1.8744	<1
Dev. from linear	12	200.7492	16.7291	
Quadratic regr.	1	179.8060	179.8060	94.44**
Dev. from quadratic	11	20.9432	1.9039	
Cubic regr.	1	3.3906	3.3906	1.93
Dev. from cubic	10	17.5526	1.7553	
Quartic regr.	1	16.1856	16.1856	106.55**
Dev. from quartic regr.	9	1.3670	0.1519	
Quintic regr.	1	0.1122	0.1122	<1
Dev. from quintic regr.	8	1.2548	0.1568	

Ideally, the sixth-degree term should be investigated to determine if it is also nonsignificant, in which case a fourth-degree regression would probably be accepted for the data. However, most authors contend that nothing much is really gained by including terms higher than the fifth degree. Consequently, tables of orthogonal polynomials contain values of ξ'_j through $j = 5$ only. One could, however, derive the values of ξ'_6 for a fixed n from the recursion formulas (7.4). In this example, however, it appears that the sixth-degree term will very likely be nonsignificant since the MS deviations are small for both the fourth- and fifth-degree terms. Further, the estimate of σ^2 using MS (deviations from fourth-degree) is smaller than the estimate using MS (deviations from fifth-degree). This occurs because the reduction in the deviation SS due to adding the fifth-degree term is not large enough to compensate for the loss of one df for the estimate of σ^2.

Using the results obtained from either Table 7.2 or Table 7.3 we are led in this case to assume that a fourth-degree regression fits the data best. The regression equation is calculated by use of Equation (7.2a) and the values of λ_j in Table 7.1. Thus,

$$\xi'_1 = 2(X - \bar{X})$$
$$\xi'_2 = \tfrac{1}{2}[(X - \bar{X})^2 - 16.250]$$
$$\xi'_3 = \tfrac{5}{3}[(X - \bar{X})^3 - 29.05(X - \bar{X})]$$
$$\xi'_4 = \tfrac{7}{12}[(X - \bar{X})^4 - 41.07(X - \bar{X})^2 + 193.26].$$

Using these values of ξ'_j, along with the calculated values of A'_j, in Equation (7.2a) yields, after algebraic simplification,

$$Y = 10.2016 + 0.3767(X - \bar{X}) - 0.3096(X - \bar{X})^2$$
$$- 0.007842(X - \bar{X})^3 + 0.006358(X - \bar{X})^4.$$

Further simplification may be obtained with the insertion of 7.5 for $\bar{X}$ and expansion.

7.5—Use of orthogonal polynomials for more than one Y-value for each X-value.

Regression analysis involving the use of orthogonal polynomials is usually illustrated in methods texts in statistics only for the case where each X value has but one Y value associated with it. In such cases, as explained above, the residual mean square has been used in practice as an estimate of experimental error although it may well be contaminated by a possibly inadequate assumed model. To properly test for lack of fit, one must know a priori the proper highest degree polynomial model specification or have some measure of error other than that provided by the residual mean square obtained from fitting a function to data where each X value has but one associated Y value. For the incompletely specified model procedure, in this case, the outcome of the preliminary test(s) may indicate that one or more of the coefficients of the powers of the independent variable, beginning with the highest, may be taken to be zero in the final fitted model. On the other hand, if the investigation provides for more than one Y observation for each X observation, then it will be possible to calculate a measure of error other than that given by the residual mean square. If there are unequal numbers of Y values for the corresponding X values, one uses the usual regression procedures for fitting a polynomial. If *equal* numbers of Y values for the corresponding X values are available, then one may use the method of orthogonal polynomials by introducing the proper multiplier into the calculations. Inference procedures for incompletely specified models, used in a similar manner, are also available for this case.

Example 7.2—Data from J. S. Hunter, "Determination of Optimum Operating Conditions by Experimental Methods, Part II–1, Models and Methods," *Industrial Quality Control*, Vol. 15, No. 6, pp. 16–24, Dec., 1958, is given in Table 7.4 in a modified form.

To meet the requirement for the use of orthogonal polynomials, that there be an *equal* number of Y values associated with each X value, we have added as a third observation the subclass mean of the respective Y values for the second, third, and fourth subclasses of Y's for the respective X values. This has been done to provide data for illustrative purposes only, hence no interpretation could be made based on the original data.

TABLE 7.4

PERCENTAGE OF IMPURITIES AT DIFFERENT TEMPERATURES

Temperature (°C)	Coded Temperature X	Per Cent of Impurities Y
200	1	6.4
200	1	5.6
200	1	6.0
210	2	7.5
210	2	6.5
210	2	7.0*
220	3	8.3
220	3	7.7
220	3	8.0*
230	4	11.7
230	4	10.3
230	4	11.0*
240	5	17.6
240	5	18.0
240	5	18.4

The experimental error sum of squares is obtained by pooling the Within Subclass sum of squares for the Subclass Y values calculated separately for each X value. Thus,

$$
\begin{aligned}
\text{SSE} = & \left[(6.4)^2 + (5.6)^2 + (6.0)^2 - \frac{(18.0)^2}{3} \right] \\
& + \left[(7.5)^2 + (6.5)^2 + (7.0)^2 - \frac{(21.0)^2}{3} \right] \\
& + \left[(8.3)^2 + (7.7)^2 + (8.0)^2 - \frac{(24.0)^2}{3} \right] \\
& + \left[(11.7)^2 + (10.3)^2 + (11.0)^2 - \frac{(33.0)^2}{3} \right] \\
& + \left[(17.6)^2 + (18.0)^2 + (18.4)^2 - \frac{(54.0)^2}{3} \right] = 2.3 \; .
\end{aligned}
$$

We now use the method of orthogonal polynomials to fit the terms of a polynomial up to the third degree to the means of the Y values for each X value for the data in Table 7.5.

TABLE 7.5

TABLE FOR CALCULATING THE POLYNOMIAL COEFFICIENTS
AND CORRESPONDING SUMS OF SQUARES ON A MEAN BASIS

$\bar{Y}$	ξ_1'	ξ_2'	ξ_3'	$\bar{Y}\xi_1'$	$\bar{Y}\xi_2'$	$\bar{Y}\xi_3'$
6.0	−2	+2	−1	−12	+12	−6
7.0	−1	−1	+2	−7	−7	+14
8.0	0	−2	0	0	−16	0
11.0	+1	−1	−2	+11	−11	−22
18.0	+2	+2	+1	+36	+36	+18
50.0	+10	+14	+10	+28	+14	+4
λ	1	1	5/6			

Then

$$A_0' = \Sigma\bar{Y}/n = 10$$
$$A_1' = \Sigma\bar{Y}\xi_1'/\Sigma(\xi_1')^2 = {}^{28}\!/_{10} = 2.8$$
$$A_2' = \Sigma\bar{Y}\xi_2'/\Sigma(\xi_2')^2 = {}^{14}\!/_{14} = 1$$
$$A_3' = \Sigma\bar{Y}\xi_3'/\Sigma(\xi_3')^2 = {}^{4}\!/_{10} = .4 .$$

Also the sums of squares on a mean basis are:

$$SSA_0' = A_0'\Sigma\bar{Y} = 10(50) = 500$$
$$SSA_1' = A_1'\Sigma\bar{Y}\xi_1' = 2.8(28) = 78.4$$
$$SSA_2' = A_2'\Sigma\bar{Y}\xi_2' = 1(14) = 14$$
$$SSA_3' = A_3'\Sigma\bar{Y}\xi_3' = .4(4) = 1.6 .$$

On a per observation basis:

$$SSA_0' = (500)(3) = 1500.0$$
$$SSA_1' = (78.4)(3) = 235.2$$
$$SSA_2' = (14)(3) = 42.0$$
$$SSA_3' = (1.6)(3) = 4.8 .$$

Then the sums of squares of deviations from regression is given by $\Sigma Y^2 - SSA_0' - SSA_1' - SSA_2' - SSA_3' = 1{,}784.30 - 1500.0 - 235.2 - 42.0 - 4.8 = 2.3$. But this happens to be precisely the value of the experimental error mean square. Hence, for this particular data, the cubic equation fits the subclass means of the Y values for each X exactly. The analysis of variance is given in Table 7.6.

TABLE 7.6
ANALYSIS OF VARIANCE FOR THE DATA OF TABLE 7.4

Source	df	SS	MS	F
Mean	1	1500.0		
Linear	1	235.2	235.20	1022.61**
Quadratic	1	42.0	42.00	182.61**
Cubic	1	4.8	4.80	20.89**
Lack of fit	1	0.0	0.00	
Experimental error	10	2.3	.23	
Total	15	1784.3		

Using formulas (7.2a) and (7.8) we find the fitted third-degree regression equation to be

$$\hat{Y} = 10 + 2.8\xi'_1 + 1\xi'_2 + 0.4\xi'_3 .$$

Using formula (7.3) and the values for λ from Table 7.5 and $\bar{X} = 3$, we find

$$\hat{Y} = 3 + 4.67X - 2.00X^2 + .33X^3 .$$

7.6—Approximate method for unequal Y subclass frequencies.

The actual data given by J. S. Hunter is available from Table 7.4 by omitting the three-starred Y values. As stated earlier one uses the usual regression methods instead of the method of orthogonal polynomials to obtain an exact analysis and inference procedures. However, in such cases one may use the method of orthogonal polynomials to obtain an approximate analysis for preliminary study.

If we omit the starred Y values in Table 7.4, then the Subclass Y means will be the same as those given in Table 7.5. Then the analysis previously given for fitting a third-degree function to these means will be the same except that the multiplier for putting the sums of squares on a per observation basis is no longer 3. It would seem appropriate to use as a multiplier the harmonic mean of the unequal subclass numbers obtained from

$$\frac{1}{\bar{n}_h} = \frac{1}{5}\left(\frac{1}{3} + \frac{1}{2} + \frac{1}{2} + \frac{1}{2} + \frac{1}{3}\right),$$

or

$$\bar{n}_h = 2.3077 .$$

The respective sums of squares are now multiplied by 2.3077 and the proper experimental error sums of squares is still 2.3 with degrees of freedom 7 instead of 10. We now obtain the approximate analysis given in Table 7.7.

TABLE 7.7
APPROXIMATE ANALYSIS OF VARIANCE

Source	df	SS	MS	F
Mean	1			
Linear	1	180.9237	180.9237	550.59 **
Quadratic	1	32.3078	32.3078	98.32 **
Cubic	1	3.6923	3.6923	11.24 *
Lack of fit	1	0.0000	0.0000	
Experimental error	7	2.3000	0.3286	

Problems

7.1—The following average heights of sunflowers, reported by Reed and Holland, are given by Snedecor (1956):

(X) Week	1	2	3	4	5	6	7	8	9	10	11	12
(Y) Height	18	36	68	98	131	170	206	228	247	250	254	254

Assume that prior information leads to a specification of a third-degree polynomial regression of Height (Y) on Week (X). Use the method of orthogonal polynomials to fit Y on a third-degree polynomial in X. Obtain the analysis of variance table, showing in turn the reduction in total sum of squares of deviations in Y due to fitting the linear, quadratic, and cubic terms. Using the residual mean square, after fitting the cubic, as the estimate of population variance, test the significance of each reduction in sum of squares, that is, each regression coefficient.

7.2—Using the data and results of Problem 7.1, plot the actual and estimated heights.

7.3—What difference, if any, would be made in the analysis and tests for Problem 7.1, if prior information had lead to a specification of a fourth-degree polynomial regression of Height (Y) on Week (X)? If different, show new analysis and tests.

7.4—Work Problem 7.3, if an incompletely specified model of fourth degree or third degree, depending upon an outcome of a preliminary test of significance at the .05 probability level, is made. Assume that the population model is actually fourth degree, but that we agree to use, for prediction, no higher than the third-degree term, if the fourth-degree regression coefficient is not significant at the .05 probability level.

7.5—Suppose, in the data in Problem 7.1, that the Y observation for $X = 5$ is missing. As a first approximation, "guess" a $Y =$ value for $X = 5$ and use an iterative procedure to fit the third-degree polynomial. Consult Pearson and Hartley (1954) for an extension of this iteration process to more complicated missing value situations.

References

Anderson, R. L., and T. A. Bancroft. 1952. *Statistical Theory in Research.* McGraw-Hill, Inc., New York.

———, and E. E. Houseman. 1942, 1963. *Tables of Orthogonal Polynomial Values Extended to N = 104.* Iowa Agriculture and Home Economics Experiment Station, Iowa State University, Ames.

Cox, C. P. 1958. A concise derivation of general orthogonal polynomials. *Journal of the Royal Statistical Society* B20:406–407.

Fisher, R. A., and F. Yates. 1953. *Statistical Tables for Biological, Agricultural and Medical Research*, 4th ed. Oliver and Boyd, Ltd., Edinburgh.

Graybill, Franklin A. 1961. *An Introduction to Linear Statistical Models.* McGraw-Hill, Inc., New York.

Kendall, M. G., and A. Stuart. 1958. *Advanced Theory of Statistics.* Hafner Publishing Co., New York.

Larson, Harold J., and T. A. Bancroft. 1963. Sequential model building for prediction in regression analysis, I. *Annals of Mathematical Statistics* 34:462–479.

———, and ———. 1963. Biases in prediction by regression for certain incompletely specified models. *Biometrika* 50:391–402.

Ostle, Bernard. 1963. *Statistics in Research*, 2nd ed. Iowa State University Press, Ames.

Pearson, E. S., and H. O. Hartley. 1954. *Biometrika Tables for Statisticians.* The Cambridge University Press, Cambridge, England.

Snedecor, George W. 1956. *Statistical Methods*, 5th ed. Iowa State University Press, Ames.

Steel, Robert, and James Torrie. 1960. *Principles and Procedures of Statistics.* McGraw-Hill, Inc., New York.

CHAPTER 8

Multiple Comparison Procedures

8.1—Introduction. It is assumed that the aim of the multiple comparison procedures discussed here is the establishment of a statement as strongly confirmed by the specific data under analysis, that is, a conclusion rather than a decision or selection. Introductory texts on statistical methods usually present several, and often differing, methods for comparing the population means two at a time after a rejection of the null hypothesis that all the population means are simultaneous equal. The multiple comparison methods in common use include: the Least Significant Difference (LSD), Scheffé's method (S), Tukey's Honestly Significant Difference (T-HSD), the Student-Newman-Keuls method (S-N-K), and Duncan's method (D). Each multiple comparison procedure is based on a particular set of assumptions and is usually effective for a specific purpose. For example, a single prechosen pair of k population means may be compared in an optimum manner by an ordinary t-test, that is, by an LSD. However, if comparisons are made that are suggested by the data, then such t-tests at a specified α significance level may no longer actually be at this significance level.

For a single classification analysis of variance with p-treatments, the number of orthogonal or independent comparisons among the population treatment means is $p - 1$, while the number of possible comparisons of such means two at a time is $p(p - 1)/2$. If p is 6, then there are only 5 independent comparisons, while there are 15 possible multiple comparisons of all treatment means taken two at a time. All of these multiple comparisons then cannot be independent, and procedures other than the simple LSD method, valid for independent comparisons, must be considered.

8.2—Scheffé's method. Scheffé's method is quite general. It may be used to test the general hypothesis that a linear function of the population means is zero or to set confidence limits for this linear function. Let $\bar{X}_i$ be estimates of the population means μ_i, with variances σ^2/n_i estimated by s^2/n_i, where s^2 has f degrees of freedom. Consider the linear function or contrast of the population means,

$$\lambda = \sum_{i=1}^{p} c_i\mu_i ,$$

where

$$\sum_{i=1}^{p} c_i = 0 .$$

The contrast is estimated by

$$\ell = \sum_{i=1}^{p} c_i\bar{x}_i .$$

If the $\bar{x}_i$ are independent, then

$$\sigma_\ell^2 = \sigma^2 \sum_{i=1}^{p} \frac{c_i^2}{n_i}$$

and the estimated variance of ℓ is

$$s_\ell^2 = s^2 \sum_{i=1}^{p} \frac{c_i^2}{n_i} .$$

Scheffé (1959) has shown that $1 - \alpha$ confidence limits for all imaginable contrasts λ may be constructed as follows:

$$P[\ell - F_0 s_\ell < \lambda < \ell + F_0 s_\ell] = 1 - \alpha \tag{8.1}$$

where

$$F_0^2 = (p - 1)F_\alpha(p - 1, f) . \tag{8.2}$$

In formula (8.2) p is the number of population means which could enter the contrast, rather than the number of means actually entering into any particular contrast. $F_\alpha(p - 1, f)$ is the tabular Snedecor F-value at the α significance level.

Since a confidence interval implies a test of significance, we may use (8.1) and (8.2) to construct a test criterion for the null hypothesis $H_0: \lambda = 0$. If $\ell > F_0 s_\ell$, reject H_0, that is, we assert that λ is significantly different from zero. As a special case we may take $c_i = 1, -1, 0, 0, \ldots, 0$, hence $\lambda = \mu_1 - \mu_2$ or more generally $\lambda = \mu_i - \mu_j$, for all i and j where $i \neq j$. In such case $\ell = \bar{x}_i - \bar{x}_j$ and

$$s_\ell^2 = s^2 \left(\frac{1}{n_i} + \frac{1}{n_j} \right),$$

and (8.1) becomes

$$P[(\bar{x}_i - \bar{x}_j) - F_0 s_\ell < \mu_i - \mu_j < (\bar{x}_i - \bar{x}_j) + F_0 s_\ell] = 1 - \alpha. \quad (8.3)$$

Further, the null hypothesis $H_0: \mu_i - \mu_j = 0$ or $\mu_i = \mu_j$ is tested by the criterion

$$\bar{x}_i - \bar{x}_j > F_0 s_\ell, \quad (8.4)$$

where the means are ranked in descending order of magnitude and $\bar{x}_i > \bar{x}_j$.

Example 8.1—Consider a one-way Model I analysis of variance. Table 8.1 gives the units in the second and third decimal places of determinations by Heyl (1930) of the gravitational constant G, for example, 83 corresponds to an observation of 6.683. Balls were made of three different materials. Heyl's data was used by Brownlee (1965), page 315–317, in a somewhat different manner.

TABLE 8.1

Units in the Second and Third Decimal Places of Determinations of the Gravitational Constant G of Balls Made of Three Different Materials

	Gold	Glass	Platinum
	83	78	61
	81	71	61
	76	75	67
	78	72	67
	79	74	64
	72		
$\bar{x}$	78.2	74.0	64.0
n	6	5	5

The resulting analysis of variance is given by Table 8.2.

TABLE 8.2

ANALYSIS OF VARIANCE

Source of Variation	df	SS	MS
Materials	2	565.105	282.553 **
Within materials	13	140.833	10.833
Total	15	705.938	

The overall test of $H_0: \mu_1 = \mu_2 = \mu_3$ is made by calculating $F = 282.533/10.833 = 26.08$ and comparing with the tabular F with 2 and 13 degrees of freedom. The calculated F is highly significant and hence we have evidence from this experiment that the population means are not all equal. To make all possible comparisons of the three population means taking them two at a time we use (8.4) in the form

$$\bar{x}_i - \bar{x}_j > \sqrt{(p - 1)F_a(p - 1, f)} \cdot \sqrt{s^2\left(\frac{1}{n_i} + \frac{1}{n_j}\right)}. \qquad (8.5)$$

Let $\bar{x}_1 = 78.2$, the gold mean; $\bar{x}_2 = 74.0$, the glass mean; and $\bar{x}_3 = 64.0$, the platinum mean. To compare $\bar{x}_1$ with $\bar{x}_3$ we investigate the correctness of the inequality

$$78.2 - 64.0 > \sqrt{(2)F_{.05}(2, 13)} \cdot \sqrt{(10.833)\left(\frac{1}{6} + \frac{1}{5}\right)},$$

or

$$14.2 > 5.5 .$$

Since the inequality holds, we have evidence from Scheffé's method that the gold population mean is different from the platinum population mean Using the same procedure we find that $78.2 - 74.0 = 4.2$ is not greater than 5.5, hence there is no evidence from this experiment that the gold population mean is different from the glass population mean. However, we find that $74.0 - 64.0 = 10$ is greater than 5.7, hence we have evidence that the glass population mean is different from the platinum population mean.

It should be noted that Scheffé's multiple comparison method is available for unequal numbers in the groups and it can be shown that it may be used for comparing means adjusted by covariance.

8.3—Multiple comparison procedures based on the studentized range. It can be seen above that Scheffé's method makes use of Snedecor's F-distribution. It can be shown that the LSD, T-HSD, S-N-K, and D methods may all be obtained from the general formula

$$\bar{x}_i - \bar{x}_j > Q(\alpha_p, p, f)s_{\bar{x}}, \qquad (8.6)$$

where $Q(\alpha_p, p, f)$ is a value to be obtained from special studentized range tables when Duncan's D method is used, that is, when $\alpha_p = 1 - (1 - \alpha)^{p-1}$, $p = 2, 3, \ldots, p$, and $f =$ degrees of freedom for the error in the analysis of variance. The method is sequential in nature, that is, a new Q value is obtained for each comparison.

The S-N-K method makes use of (8.6) with $\alpha_p = \alpha$, a constant; $p = 2, 3, \ldots, p$; and f as error degrees of freedom. This method is also sequential in nature and $Q(\alpha, p, f)$ values are obtained from an ordinary studentized range table. On the other hand the T-HSD method is not sequential in nature, but makes use of an ordinary Q value where $\alpha_p = a$, $p = p$, and $f =$ degrees of freedom of error as usual. The LSD method is also nonsequential, with $\alpha_p = \alpha$, $p = 2$, and $f =$ degrees of freedom of error as usual.

In general, all the multiple comparison methods above, based on the special or ordinary studentized range table, are exact only for equal numbers in the groups and for means that have not been adjusted by covariance. This is in contrast, as noted earlier, to Scheffé's multiple comparison method which is exact for means based on unequal as well as equal size samples $(n_i \neq n_j)$ and for means that have been adjusted by covariance. However, as will be illustrated, the generality of the S method must be paid for by the small number of differences declared significant on the average as compared with the multiple comparison procedures based on the studentized range.

Example 8.2—Duncan (1955) gives the following results for a varietal experiment.

TABLE 8.3

ANALYSIS OF VARIANCE

Source of Variation	df	MS	Calculated F
Among blocks	5	141.95	
Among varieties	6	366.97	4.61
Error	30	79.64	

Varietal means in ranked order were: $A(49.6)$, $F(58.1)$, $G(61.0)$, $D(61.5)$, $C(67.6)$, $B(71.2)$, $E(71.3)$. We calculate $s_{\bar{x}} = \sqrt{79.64/6} = 3.643$. Now, there are $\binom{7}{2} = 21$ possible comparisons of the means taken two at a time. Using the LSD method, we employ the formula $\bar{x}_i - \bar{x}_j > t(.05,$

30)$\sqrt{2}\ s_{\bar{x}} = Q(.05, 2, 30)s_{\bar{x}} = (2.89)(3.643) = 10.518$, and find 7 significant differences: E-A, B-A, C-A, D-A, G-A, E-F, and B-F. Using Tukey's method, we employ the formula $\bar{x}_i - \bar{x}_j > Q(.05, 7, 30)s_{\bar{x}} = (4.46)(3.643) = 16.248$, and find 3 significant differences: E-A, B-A, and C-A. Using the Student-Newman-Keuls method, we employ the formula $\bar{x}_i - \bar{x}_j > Q(.05, p, 30)s_{\bar{x}} = Q(.05, p, 30)(3.463)$ and find 3 significant differences: E-A, B-A, and C-A. Note that the S-N-K method is sequential in nature, requiring a different tabular value of $Q(.05, p, 30)$ as p takes the values 2, 3, 4, . . . , 7. Using Duncan's method, we employ the formula $\bar{x}_i - \bar{x}_j > Q(\alpha_p, p, 30)s_{\bar{x}} = Q(\alpha, p, 30)(3.643)$ and find 7 significant differences: E-A, B-A, C-A, D-A, G-A, E-F, and B-F. Duncan's method is also sequential in nature, with $p = 2, 3, . . . , 7$ and $\alpha_p = 1 - (1 - \alpha)^{p-1}$. Note that only one and the same table is required for the LSD, T-HSD, and the S-N-K methods, whereas a different table is required for the D method. Using Scheffé's method, we employ the formula $\bar{x}_i - \bar{x}_j > \sqrt{6F_{.05}(6, 30)} \cdot \sqrt{2}\ s_{\bar{x}} = \sqrt{6(2.42)} \cdot (1.414)(3.643) = 19.61$, and find 2 significant differences: E-A and B-A.

8.4—Difficulty of assessing the relative merits of multiple comparison procedures.

In testing a hypothesis involving a simple two-decision situation, such as that to which the Neyman-Pearson theory is directly applicable, one compares two competing test criteria by fixing the Type I errors to be the same for both and comparing the two power curves. Unfortunately, multiple-comparison procedures do not pertain to a single simple two-decision situation, but are special cases of *multiple*-decision procedures. At present there is no generally acceptable analytical method of comparing, in a manner similar to that for the two-decision situation, two competing multiple-decision test criteria.

Attempts have been made by Tukey (1953) to clarify the problem of the multiple comparison of means by recognizing different definitions of Type I errors in this situation. For example, we define the

(1) Per-comparison error rate as the long-run value of

$$\frac{\text{Number of comparisons falsely declared significant}}{\text{Total number of comparisons}},$$

and the

(2) Experimentwise error rate as the long-run value of

$$\frac{\text{Number of experiments with at least one difference falsely declared significant}}{\text{Total number of experiments}}.$$

Using the above definitions, empirical studies have been undertaken to compare the size and power of multiple-comparison methods for various assumed relations among the populations means (see for example Chen, 1960). However, for the comparison of any appreciable number of population means there are many differing ways that the means may be unequal, hence it is unlikely that the results of such studies of power comparisons could be made useful and practical for all needs. Nevertheless, such definitions as (1) and (2) above, and the empirical studies, do provide some assistance in appraising the characteristics of the various competing multiple-comparison procedures.

Chen's empirical study revealed that the ranking from high to low of control of the error rate per comparison for four 5% multiple-comparison procedures was as follows: LSD, Duncan, Student-Newman-Keul, and Tukey. A similar ranking from high to low of control of the experimentwise error rate of these four 5% multiple-comparison procedures was as follows: Tukey and Student-Newman-Keul, Duncan, and LSD. In view of such results a choice of a multiple-comparison procedure, based on a proper control of size in a particular experiment, would depend upon the importance attached to using the whole experiment (experimentwise error rate) to arrive at a conclusion versus that attached to the individual comparison (per-comparison error rate).

Chen's empirical study of power was based on sampling from k normal populations of homogeneous population variances and only one population mean different from the other $k - 1$ equal population means. (Note that, in the empirical size studies mentioned earlier, all k population means would be made equal.)

Chen defined the empirical power—for each multiple-comparison procedure for testing the true difference $D_{ij} = \mu_i - \mu_j = (\mu + \Delta_i) - (\mu + \Delta_j) = \Delta_i - \Delta_j$ and $i, j = 1, 2, \ldots, k; i \neq j$— as the proportion of the differences of the corresponding sample means, $d_{ij} = \bar{x}_i - \bar{x}_j$, declared significant for each corresponding procedure in the whole set of 100 experiments. In the special case when only one population mean is different from the other $k - 1$ equal population means, there are $k - 1$ comparisons having the same true difference Δ, that is, $D_{ij} = (\mu + \Delta) - (\mu) = \Delta$. The powers of the $k - 1$ tests for these comparisons for each procedure are expected to be the same because of symmetry of the testing procedure, therefore Chen averaged their empirical power values in his study of the multiple-comparison procedures. For this very special case, and the definitions adopted for empirical power, Chen's study revealed the following ranking from high to low for his kind of empirical power: LSD, Duncan, Student-Newman-Keuls, and Tukey. It should be kept in mind that this power ranking is for a very special case only. Note that Chen's study of size and power did not include Scheffé's procedure.

8.5—Summary and recommendations. Since the LSD yields a relatively very high experimentwise error rate, it is usually not recommended for multiple comparison of all pairs of population means from an experiment. Used for this purpose it tends in general to be overly sensitive in declaring a large number of differences in a particular experiment as significant at the expense of committing more Type I errors.

Duncan attempts to justify his new multiple-range test by analogy with a test procedure that would be optimum in sets of independent tests. Next to the LSD, Duncan's procedure is expected, in general, to be sensitive in declaring a relatively large number of differences as significant. In view of the approximate character of this multiple-comparison procedure, it has not found ready acceptance among many mathematical statisticians. Even so, in certain kinds of agronomic or animal husbandry experiments, Duncan's new multiple-range procedures are preferred due to the fact that in such cases the characteristics of the varieties or lines to be tested may be already recognized to some extent by the experimenter through preliminary tests or through the records of their pedigrees. Hence, if the experimenter feels that some true differences between varieties or lines should exist, he may well wish to use a less cautious testing procedure in order to reveal the true situation. This situation may not exist, however, in other kinds of research.

The Student-Newman-Keuls procedure does not have the approximate character of Duncan's procedure. Chen's empirical study revealed that the S-N-K procedure is less powerful and more conservative in the number of differences declared significant than the D procedure. In situations in which it is not necessary to be so conservative, Hartley (1955) has suggested use of the S-N-K procedure with the significance level test of 10% or even higher. Chen's empirical study showed that for the special case considered, the S-N-K procedure controlled the experimentwise error at the desired level. A disadvantage of the S-N-K procedure is that its power of testing the differences of all pairs of means is definitely subject to the magnitudes of the other true means. This means that different results might be obtained in comparing two particular population means by an S-N-K procedure applied to one set of population means including the two in question as contrasted with a second set, also including the two in question, but with the other means of different magnitude.

Chen's empirical study showed that Tukey's procedure controlled the experimentwise error at the desired level. The empirical study, however, revealed it to be the last of the multiple-comparison procedures using the studentized range in controlling error rate per comparison and in controlling the empirical power as defined by Chen. The T-HSD procedure is useful, however, in situations in which one may wish to place primary emphasis on the use of the experiment as a whole in determining significance of the pairs of population means or in setting confidence interval for differences in the population means.

Since Scheffé's procedure has been designed to compare all possible linear functions of a set of population means, including comparison of the means two at a time, this procedure is quite conservative in the number of such comparison's declared significant—as is to be expected. It is usually less to be preferred than Tukey's procedure for multiple comparisons of pairs of p population means, but may be preferred to Tukey's procedure for other multiple-linear comparisons of population means. It is of importance to remember that, in comparison with the S-N-K, Duncan, and Tukey procedures, only the S procedure is exact for comparison of population means based on unequal sample sizes or for comparison of population means adjusted by linear covariance. The difficulty arises because the other procedures require equal variances and independence of the population means.

8.6—Multiple comparison procedures for unequal size samples. The LSD procedure may be easily modified for use when the sample means are computed from unequal size samples. The modified LSD method calls for use of the formula

$$\bar{x}_i - \bar{x}_j > t(\alpha, \gamma)s \sqrt{\frac{1}{n_i} + \frac{1}{n_j}},$$

where s^2 is the pooled sum of squares of deviations divided by the pooled degrees of freedom.

As was illustrated in Section 8.2, Scheffé's procedure is also applicable in the case of unequal size samples.

There appears to be no method of modifying the S-N-K, T-HSD, and D procedures to yield exact multiple comparisons for all pairs of population means for unequal sample sizes. In the absence of modifications resulting in exact procedures for these tests using the studentized range, one may wish to try modifications producing approximate procedures. One such intuitive modification would involve using $s_{\bar{x}} = s/\sqrt{\bar{n}_h}$, where

$$\frac{1}{\bar{n}_h} = \frac{1}{p}\left(\frac{1}{n_1} + \frac{1}{n_2} + \cdots + \frac{1}{n_p}\right)$$

and n_i is the number of observations used to calculate each sample mean $\bar{x}_i$. Using this approximation, the general formula (8.6) becomes

$$\bar{x}_i - \bar{x}_j > Q(\alpha_p, p, f)s/\sqrt{\bar{n}_h}. \tag{8.7}$$

As an illustration let us use Tukey's special form of (8.7) on the data in Table 8.1. We calculate

$$\frac{1}{\bar{n}_h} = \frac{1}{3}\left(\frac{1}{6} + \frac{1}{5} + \frac{1}{5}\right) = \frac{17}{90}.$$

Then the right hand side of (8.7) becomes

$$Q(.05, 3, 13)\sqrt{(10.833)\left(\frac{17}{90}\right)} = (3.73)(1.43) = 5.33.$$

In this case we have evidence that the gold population mean is greater than the platinum population mean, also that the glass population mean is greater than the platinum population mean. In this case the approximate use of Tukey's procedure yields the same inferences as Scheffé's exact procedure. Formula (8.7) becomes more nearly exact as the n_i become more nearly equal.

8.7—Multiple comparison procedures for means adjusted by covariance. Snedecor (1956) gives the results of a covariance analysis of a completely randomized pig nutrition experiment for four different treatments applied to 10 pigs in each group. The variables measured were initial weight X and average daily gain Y. The adjusted Y-means, Y_A, and corresponding X-means are given in Table 8.4.

TABLE 8.4

ADJUSTED Y-MEANS AND CORRESPONDING X-MEANS
(Treatments)

Treatments Means	1	2	3	4
$\bar{Y}_A$	1.65	1.49	1.31	1.19
$\bar{X}$	54.0	50.5	50.7	53.2

As mentioned earlier Scheffé's procedure provides an exact method of comparing all pairs of adjusted means. We find

$$\ell = \bar{y}'_i - \bar{y}'_j = \bar{y}_i - \bar{y}_j - b(\bar{x}_i - \bar{x}_j) \,,$$

where $\bar{y}'_i$ and $\bar{y}'_j$ are any two adjusted means. Then

$$s_\ell^2 = s_{y.x}^2 \left[\frac{2}{n} + \frac{(\bar{x}_i - \bar{x}_j)^2}{\Sigma x_E^2} \right],$$

where $s_{y.x}^2$ is the error mean square and Σx_E^2 is the sum of square of x given in the covariance analysis by Snedecor as 0.02123 and 4262, respectively. Then for treatments 1 and 2 in Table 8.2 we find

$$s_\ell^2 = 0.02123 \left[\frac{2}{10} + \frac{(54.0 - 50.5)^2}{4262} \right] = 0.00431 \,,$$

and

$$s_\ell = 0.0657 \,.$$

Making use of Scheffé's procedure by using (8.4) we find

$$\bar{y}'_1 - \bar{y}'_2 > F_0 s_\ell$$
$$> \sqrt{(4-1)(2.87)} \, (0.0657)$$
$$> .19 \,.$$

But $\bar{Y}'_1 - \bar{Y}'_2 = .16$, which is not greater than .19, hence we have no evidence that adjusted population treatment means 1 and 2 are unequal. The other pairs of means may be compared in a similar fashion.

Since the adjusted means will not in general have equal variances or equal covariances, even if the number of observations in each group is the same, there appears to be no method of modifying the S-N-K, T-HSD, and D procedures to yield exact multiple comparisons of all pairs of adjusted population means. Should one wish to consider approximate methods for such multiple comparison procedures, it will be necessary to rewrite (8.6) as

$$\bar{y}'_i - \bar{y}'_j > Q(\alpha_p, p, f)\bar{s}_{\bar{y}'} , \qquad (8.8)$$

where $\bar{y}'_i$ and $\bar{y}'_j$ are two adjusted means and the standard error of an adjusted mean, $\bar{s}_{y'}$, must be some approximate average standard error of an adjusted mean. Making use of suggestions made by Finney (1946) and Cochran and Cox (1957), Snedecor (1956) recommends using

$$\bar{s}_{\bar{y}'} = \sqrt{\frac{s^2_{y.x}}{n}\left[1 + \frac{\Sigma x^2_T}{(t-1)\Sigma x^2_E}\right]} , \qquad (8.9)$$

where Σx^2_T is the x sum of squares for treatments. Using the data from the pig nutrition experiment,

$$\bar{s}_{\bar{y}'} = \sqrt{\frac{0.0212}{10}\left[1 + \frac{94}{3(4,262)}\right]} = 0.046 .$$

Using Tukey's procedure, which now is approximate, we calculate $Q(.05,4,35)\bar{s}_{\bar{y}'} = (3.81)(0.046) = 0.18$, and find significant differences between the following adjusted means: 1 and 4, 1 and 3, 2 and 4, and 2 and 3.

8.8—Comparing treatment means with a control mean.

Dunnett (1955) has developed a valid multiple-comparison procedure for the important special case where we have tested $1 + t$ population means in an analysis of variance, of which one is a control and we wish to compare the other t with the control. The t comparisons with the control are not independent, hence the LSD procedure is not wholly valid. To apply Dunnett's procedure we calculate

$$D = ds_{\bar{x}_a - \bar{x}_i} , \qquad (8.10)$$

where d is a quantity obtained by entering Dunnett's special tables (1955, 1964) for a one-sided or two-sided test as required, desired error rate, number of treatments t, and error degrees of freedom. As an example, suppose we use the data in Table 8.1 and consider the glass mean as the control. For a two-sided test for comparing the gold mean with control we calculate $(2.48) \sqrt{10.833(1/6 + 1/5)} = 4.94$ and note that it is greater than $78.2 - 74.0 = 4.2$. Hence we have no evidence that the population gold mean is greater than control. Similarly we calculate $2.48\sqrt{10.833(2/5)} = 5.16$, and note that it is less than $74.0 - 64.0 = 10.0$. Hence we have evidence that the population platinum mean is less than control. Note that $\bar{X}_a$, the control mean, does not necessarily have to be based on the same number of observations as $\bar{X}_i$.

Problems

8.1—Assume that there is no interaction in the linear model specification for Example 1.1. Using the Within MS from Table 1.3 as an estimate of error, make all possible comparisons of the phosphate (P) means, at the nominal .05 significance level, by each of the following multiple-comparison procedures: (1) LSD, (2) D, (3) S-N-K, (4) T-HSD, and (5) S. (Note that the multiple-comparison procedures are being used in this case for a two-way classification in a manner which is similar to the use of such procedures made for the data in Table 8.3.)

8.2—Would the inferences obtained in Problem 8.1 be the same if the pooled MS for Within and NP in Table 1.3 should be used as an estimate of error?

8.3—Comment on the appropriateness or not of the choice of error made for Problems 8.1 and 8.2. Under what conditions should the MS for NP alone be considered as a proper choice for an estimate of error?

8.4—Using the approximate method illustrated in Section 8.6 for the T-HSD procedure and the data from Table 8.1, compare the three means two at a time by the following procedures: (1) D and (2) S-N-K.

8.5—With the assumptions made in Problem 8.1, consider the mean for P_0 as control and compare the means of P_1 and P_2 with that of P_0 by using Dunnett's procedure.

8.6—Using the values given in Table 8.2, make all remaining possible comparisons of the pairs of adjusted means by using Scheffé's exact procedure. Use (8.8) to obtain the remaining approximate comparisons for the T-HSD procedure. Use the formula (8.8) to obtain all such comparisons approximately for the S-N-K procedure. Compare the inferences obtained from these three procedures.

References

Brownlee, K. A. 1965. *Statistical Theory and Methodology in Science and Engineering.* John Wiley & Sons, Inc., New York.

Chen, Ta-chuan. 1960. Multiple comparisons of population means. Unpublished M.S. thesis, Iowa State University, Ames.

Cochran, W. G., and G. M. Cox. 1957. *Design and Analysis of Experiments*. John Wiley & Sons, Inc., New York.

Duncan, David B. 1955. Multiple range and multiple *F* tests. *Biometrics* 11:1–42.

———. 1955. Multiple range tests for correlated and heteroscedastic means. *Biometrics* 13:164–176.

———. 1961. Bayes rules for a common multiple comparisons problem and related Student *t* problems. *Annals of Mathematical Statistics* 32:1013–1033.

Dunn, O. J. 1961. Multiple comparisons among means. *Journal of the American Statistical Association* 56:52–64.

Dunnett, Charles W. 1955. A multiple comparison procedure for comparing several treatments with a control. *Journal of the American Statistical Association* 50:1096–1121.

———. 1964. New tables for multiple comparisons with a control. *Biometrics* 20:482–491.

Federer, W. T. 1965. Query 11, Error rate bases. *Technometrics* 7:260–262. Also, all articles in *Technometrics* 7.

Finney, D. J. 1946. Standard errors of yields adjusted for regression on an independent measurement. *Biometrics* (Bulletin) 2:53–55.

Harter, H. Leon. 1957. Error rates and sample sizes for range tests in multiple comparisons. *Biometrics* 13:511–536.

———. 1960. Critical values for Duncan's new multiple range test. *Biometrics* 16:671–685.

Hartley, H. O. 1955. Some recent developments in analysis of variance. *Communication on Pure and Applied Mathematics* 8:47–72.

Heyl, Paul R. 1930. A redetermination of the constant of gravitation. *Journal of Research of the Bureau of Standards* 5:1243–1250.

Keuls, M. 1952. The use of the studentized range in connection with the analysis of variance. *Euphytica* 1:112–122.

Kramer, Clyde Y. 1956. Extension of multiple range tests to group means with unequal numbers of replications. *Biometrics* 12:307–310.

———. 1957. Extension of multiple range tests to group correlated adjusted means. *Biometrics* 13:13–18.

Miller, Rupert G., Jr. 1966. *Simultaneous Statistical Inference*. McGraw-Hill, Inc., New York.

Newman, D. 1939. The distribution of the range in samples from a normal population in terms of an independent estimate of standard deviation. *Biometrika* 31:20–30.

Scheflé, Henry. 1953. A method for judging all contrast in the analysis of variance. *Biometrika* 40:87–104.

———. 1959. *Analysis of Variance*. John Wiley & Sons, Inc., New York.

Snedecor, George W. 1956. *Statistical Methods*. 5th ed. Iowa State University Press, Ames.

Tukey, John W. 1949. Comparing individual means in the analysis of variance. *Biometrics* 5:99–114.

———. 1953. The problem of multiple comparisons. Unpublished notes, Princeton University, 396 pp.

Wine, R. L. 1955. A power study of multiple range and multiple *F* tests. Unpublished Ph.D. thesis, Virginia Polytechnic Institute, Blacksburg.

Appendix: Tables

TABLE I

ACCUMULATIVE DISTRIBUTION OF CHI-SQUARE

Degrees of Freedom	Probability of a Greater Value												
	0.995	0.990	0.975	0.950	0.900	0.750	0.500	0.250	0.100	0.050	0.025	0.010	0.005
1	. . .	. . .	. . .	. . .	0.02	0.10	0.45	1.32	2.71	3.84	5.02	6.63	7.88
2	0.01	0.02	0.05	0.10	0.21	0.58	1.39	2.77	4.61	5.99	7.38	9.21	10.60
3	0.07	0.11	0.22	0.35	0.58	1.21	2.37	4.11	6.25	7.81	9.35	11.34	12.84
4	0.21	0.30	0.48	0.71	1.06	1.92	3.36	5.39	7.78	9.49	11.14	13.28	14.86
5	0.41	0.55	0.83	1.15	1.61	2.67	4.35	6.63	9.24	11.07	12.83	15.09	16.75
6	0.68	0.87	1.24	1.64	2.20	3.45	5.35	7.84	10.64	12.59	14.45	16.81	18.55
7	0.99	1.24	1.69	2.17	2.83	4.25	6.35	9.04	12.02	14.07	16.01	18.48	20.28
8	1.34	1.65	2.18	2.73	3.49	5.07	7.34	10.22	13.36	15.51	17.53	20.09	21.96
9	1.73	2.09	2.70	3.33	4.17	5.90	8.34	11.39	14.68	16.92	19.02	21.67	23.59
10	2.16	2.56	3.25	3.94	4.87	6.74	9.34	12.55	15.99	18.31	20.48	23.21	25.19
11	2.60	3.05	3.82	4.57	5.58	7.58	10.34	13.70	17.28	19.68	21.92	24.72	26.76
12	3.07	3.57	4.40	5.23	6.30	8.44	11.34	14.85	18.55	21.03	23.34	26.22	28.30
13	3.57	4.11	5.01	5.89	7.04	9.30	12.34	15.98	19.81	22.36	24.74	27.69	29.82
14	4.07	4.66	5.63	6.57	7.79	10.17	13.34	17.12	21.06	23.68	26.12	29.14	31.32
15	4.60	5.23	6.27	7.26	8.55	11.04	14.34	18.25	22.31	25.00	27.49	30.58	32.80
16	5.14	5.81	6.91	7.96	9.31	11.91	15.34	19.37	23.54	26.30	28.85	32.00	34.27
17	5.70	6.41	7.56	8.67	10.09	12.79	16.34	20.49	24.77	27.59	30.19	33.41	35.72
18	6.26	7.01	8.23	9.39	10.86	13.68	17.34	21.60	25.99	28.87	31.53	34.81	37.16
19	6.84	7.63	8.91	10.12	11.65	14.56	18.34	22.72	27.20	30.14	32.85	36.19	38.58
20	7.43	8.26	9.59	10.85	12.44	15.45	19.34	23.83	28.41	31.41	34.17	37.57	40.00
21	8.03	8.90	10.28	11.59	13.24	16.34	20.34	24.93	29.62	32.67	35.48	38.93	41.40
22	8.64	9.54	10.98	12.34	14.04	17.24	21.34	26.04	30.81	33.92	36.78	40.29	42.80
23	9.26	10.20	11.69	13.09	14.85	18.14	22.34	27.14	32.01	35.17	38.08	41.64	44.18
24	9.89	10.86	12.40	13.85	15.66	19.04	23.34	28.24	33.20	36.42	39.36	42.98	45.56
25	10.52	11.52	13.12	14.61	16.47	19.94	24.34	29.34	34.38	37.65	40.65	44.31	46.93
26	11.16	12.20	13.84	15.38	17.29	20.84	25.34	30.43	35.56	38.89	41.92	45.64	48.29
27	11.81	12.88	14.57	16.15	18.11	21.75	26.34	31.53	36.74	40.11	43.19	46.96	49.64
28	12.46	13.56	15.31	16.93	18.94	22.66	27.34	32.62	37.92	41.34	44.46	48.28	50.99
29	13.12	14.26	16.05	17.71	19.77	23.57	28.34	33.71	39.09	42.56	45.72	49.59	52.34
30	13.79	14.95	16.79	18.49	20.60	24.48	29.34	34.80	40.26	43.77	46.98	50.89	53.67
40	20.71	22.16	24.43	26.51	29.05	33.66	39.34	45.62	51.80	55.76	59.34	63.69	66.77
50	27.99	29.71	32.36	34.76	37.69	42.94	49.33	56.33	63.17	67.50	71.42	76.15	79.49
60	35.53	37.48	40.48	43.19	46.46	52.29	59.33	66.98	74.40	79.08	83.30	88.38	91.95
70	43.28	45.44	48.76	51.74	55.33	61.70	69.33	77.58	85.53	90.53	95.02	100.42	104.22
80	51.17	53.54	57.15	60.39	64.28	71.14	79.33	88.13	96.58	101.88	106.63	112.33	116.32
90	59.20	61.75	65.65	69.13	73.29	80.62	89.33	98.64	107.56	113.14	118.14	124.12	128.30
100	67.33	70.06	74.22	77.93	82.36	90.13	99.33	109.14	118.50	124.34	129.56	135.81	140.17

Source: Condensed from table with 6 significant figures by Catherine M. Thompson, by permission of the Editor of *Biometrika* (11).

TABLE II

The Distribution of t

Degrees of Freedom	Probability of a Larger Value, Sign Ignored								
	0.500	0.400	0.200	0.100	0.050	0.025	0.010	0.005	0.001
1	1.000	1.376	3.078	6.314	12.706	25.452	63.657		
2	.816	1.061	1.886	2.920	4.303	6.205	9.925	14.089	31.598
3	.765	.978	1.638	2.353	3.182	4.176	5.841	7.453	12.941
4	.741	.941	1.533	2.132	2.776	3.495	4.604	5.598	8.610
5	.727	.920	1.476	2.015	2.571	3.163	4.032	4.773	6.859
6	.718	.906	1.440	1.943	2.447	2.969	3.707	4.317	5.959
7	.711	.896	1.415	1.895	2.365	2.841	3.499	4.029	5.405
8	.706	.889	1.397	1.860	2.306	2.752	3.355	3.832	5.041
9	.703	.883	1.383	1.833	2.262	2.685	3.250	3.690	4.781
10	.700	.879	1.372	1.812	2.228	2.634	3.169	3.581	4.587
11	.697	.876	1.363	1.796	2.201	2.593	3.106	3.497	4.437
12	.695	.873	1.356	1.782	2.179	2.560	3.055	3.428	4.318
13	.694	.870	1.350	1.771	2.160	2.533	3.012	3.372	4.221
14	.692	.868	1.345	1.761	2.145	2.510	2.977	3.326	4.140
15	.691	.866	1.341	1.753	2.131	2.490	2.947	3.286	4.073
16	.690	.865	1.337	1.746	2.120	2.473	2.921	3.252	4.015
17	.689	.863	1.333	1.740	2.110	2.458	2.898	3.222	3.965
18	.688	.862	1.330	1.734	2.101	2.445	2.878	3.197	3.922
19	.688	.861	1.328	1.729	2.093	2.433	2.861	3.174	3.883
20	.687	.860	1.325	1.725	2.086	2.423	2.845	3.153	3.850
21	.686	.859	1.323	1.721	2.080	2.414	2.831	3.135	3.819
22	.686	.858	1.321	1.717	2.074	2.406	2.819	3.119	3.792
23	.685	.858	1.319	1.714	2.069	2.398	2.807	3.104	3.767
24	.685	.857	1.318	1.711	2.064	2.391	2.797	3.090	3.745
25	.684	.856	1.316	1.708	2.060	2.385	2.787	3.078	3.725
26	.684	.856	1.315	1.706	2.056	2.379	2.779	3.067	3.707
27	.684	.855	1.314	1.703	2.052	2.373	2.771	3.056	3.690
28	.683	.855	1.313	1.701	2.048	2.368	2.763	3.047	3.674
29	.683	.854	1.311	1.699	2.045	2.364	2.756	3.038	3.659
30	.683	.854	1.310	1.697	2.042	2.360	2.750	3.030	3.646
35	.682	.852	1.306	1.690	2.030	2.342	2.724	2.996	3.591
40	.681	.851	1.303	1.684	2.021	2.329	2.704	2.971	3.551
45	.680	.850	1.301	1.680	2.014	2.319	2.690	2.952	3.520
50	.680	.849	1.299	1.676	2.008	2.310	2.678	2.937	3.496
55	.679	.849	1.297	1.673	2.004	2.304	2.669	2.925	3.476
60	.679	.848	1.296	1.671	2.000	2.299	2.660	2.915	3.460
70	.678	.847	1.294	1.667	1.994	2.290	2.648	2.899	3.435
80	.678	.847	1.293	1.665	1.989	2.284	2.638	2.887	3.416
90	.678	.846	1.291	1.662	1.986	2.279	2.631	2.878	3.402
100	.677	.846	1.290	1.661	1.982	2.276	2.625	2.871	3.390
120	.677	.845	1.289	1.658	1.980	2.270	2.617	2.860	3.373
∞	.6745	.8416	1.2816	1.6448	1.9600	2.2414	2.5758	2.8070	3.2905

Source: Parts of this table are reprinted by permission from R. A. Fisher's *Statistical Methods for Research Workers*, published by Oliver and Boyd, Edinburgh (1925–1950); from Maxine Merrington's "Table of percentage points of the t-distribution," *Biometrika*, 32:300 (1942); and from Bernard Ostle's *Statistics in Research*, Iowa State University Press, p. 528 (1963).

TABLE III
Percentage Points of the F-Distribution
Upper 25% Points

v_2 \ v_1	1	2	3	4	5	6	7	8	9	10	12	15	20	24	30	40	60	120	∞
1	5.83	7.50	8.20	8.58	8.82	8.98	9.10	9.19	9.26	9.32	9.41	9.49	9.58	9.63	9.67	9.71	9.76	9.80	9.85
2	2.57	3.00	3.15	3.23	3.28	3.31	3.34	3.35	3.37	3.38	3.39	3.41	3.43	3.43	3.44	3.45	3.46	3.47	3.48
3	2.02	2.28	2.36	2.39	2.41	2.42	2.43	2.44	2.44	2.44	2.45	2.46	2.46	2.46	2.47	2.47	2.47	2.47	2.47
4	1.81	2.00	2.05	2.06	2.07	2.08	2.08	2.08	2.08	2.08	2.08	2.08	2.08	2.08	2.08	2.08	2.08	2.08	2.08
5	1.69	1.85	1.88	1.89	1.89	1.89	1.89	1.89	1.89	1.89	1.89	1.89	1.88	1.88	1.88	1.88	1.87	1.87	1.87
6	1.62	1.76	1.78	1.79	1.79	1.78	1.78	1.78	1.77	1.77	1.77	1.76	1.76	1.75	1.75	1.75	1.74	1.74	1.74
7	1.57	1.70	1.72	1.72	1.71	1.71	1.70	1.70	1.69	1.69	1.68	1.68	1.67	1.67	1.66	1.66	1.65	1.65	1.65
8	1.54	1.66	1.67	1.66	1.66	1.65	1.64	1.64	1.63	1.63	1.62	1.62	1.61	1.60	1.60	1.59	1.59	1.58	1.58
9	1.51	1.62	1.63	1.63	1.62	1.61	1.60	1.60	1.59	1.59	1.58	1.57	1.56	1.56	1.55	1.54	1.54	1.53	1.53
10	1.49	1.60	1.60	1.59	1.59	1.58	1.57	1.56	1.56	1.55	1.54	1.53	1.52	1.52	1.51	1.51	1.50	1.49	1.48
11	1.47	1.58	1.58	1.57	1.56	1.55	1.54	1.53	1.53	1.52	1.51	1.50	1.49	1.49	1.48	1.47	1.47	1.46	1.45
12	1.46	1.56	1.56	1.55	1.54	1.53	1.52	1.51	1.51	1.50	1.49	1.48	1.47	1.46	1.45	1.45	1.44	1.43	1.42
13	1.45	1.55	1.55	1.53	1.52	1.51	1.50	1.49	1.49	1.48	1.47	1.46	1.45	1.44	1.43	1.42	1.42	1.41	1.40
14	1.44	1.53	1.53	1.52	1.51	1.50	1.49	1.48	1.47	1.46	1.45	1.44	1.43	1.42	1.41	1.41	1.40	1.39	1.38
15	1.43	1.52	1.52	1.51	1.49	1.48	1.47	1.46	1.46	1.45	1.44	1.43	1.41	1.41	1.40	1.39	1.38	1.37	1.36
16	1.42	1.51	1.51	1.50	1.48	1.47	1.46	1.45	1.44	1.44	1.43	1.41	1.40	1.39	1.38	1.37	1.36	1.35	1.34
17	1.42	1.51	1.50	1.49	1.47	1.46	1.45	1.44	1.43	1.43	1.41	1.40	1.39	1.38	1.37	1.36	1.35	1.34	1.33
18	1.41	1.50	1.49	1.48	1.46	1.45	1.44	1.43	1.42	1.42	1.40	1.39	1.38	1.37	1.36	1.35	1.34	1.33	1.32
19	1.41	1.49	1.49	1.47	1.46	1.44	1.43	1.42	1.41	1.41	1.40	1.38	1.37	1.36	1.35	1.34	1.33	1.32	1.30
20	1.40	1.49	1.48	1.47	1.45	1.44	1.43	1.42	1.41	1.40	1.39	1.37	1.36	1.35	1.34	1.33	1.32	1.31	1.29
21	1.40	1.48	1.48	1.46	1.44	1.43	1.42	1.41	1.40	1.39	1.38	1.37	1.35	1.34	1.33	1.32	1.31	1.30	1.28
22	1.40	1.48	1.47	1.45	1.44	1.42	1.41	1.40	1.39	1.39	1.37	1.36	1.34	1.33	1.32	1.31	1.30	1.29	1.28
23	1.39	1.47	1.47	1.45	1.43	1.42	1.41	1.40	1.39	1.38	1.37	1.35	1.34	1.33	1.32	1.31	1.30	1.28	1.27
24	1.39	1.47	1.46	1.44	1.43	1.41	1.40	1.39	1.38	1.38	1.36	1.35	1.33	1.32	1.31	1.30	1.29	1.28	1.26
25	1.39	1.47	1.46	1.44	1.42	1.41	1.40	1.39	1.38	1.37	1.36	1.34	1.33	1.32	1.31	1.29	1.28	1.27	1.25
26	1.38	1.46	1.45	1.44	1.42	1.41	1.39	1.38	1.37	1.37	1.35	1.34	1.32	1.31	1.30	1.29	1.28	1.26	1.25
27	1.38	1.46	1.45	1.43	1.42	1.40	1.39	1.38	1.37	1.36	1.35	1.33	1.32	1.31	1.30	1.28	1.27	1.26	1.24
28	1.38	1.46	1.45	1.43	1.41	1.40	1.39	1.38	1.37	1.36	1.34	1.33	1.31	1.30	1.29	1.28	1.27	1.25	1.24
29	1.38	1.45	1.45	1.43	1.41	1.40	1.38	1.37	1.36	1.35	1.34	1.32	1.31	1.30	1.29	1.27	1.26	1.25	1.23
30	1.38	1.45	1.44	1.42	1.41	1.39	1.38	1.37	1.36	1.35	1.34	1.32	1.30	1.29	1.28	1.27	1.26	1.24	1.23
40	1.36	1.44	1.42	1.40	1.39	1.37	1.36	1.35	1.34	1.33	1.31	1.30	1.28	1.26	1.25	1.24	1.22	1.21	1.19
60	1.35	1.42	1.41	1.38	1.37	1.35	1.33	1.32	1.31	1.30	1.29	1.27	1.25	1.24	1.22	1.21	1.19	1.17	1.15
120	1.34	1.40	1.39	1.37	1.35	1.33	1.31	1.30	1.29	1.28	1.26	1.24	1.22	1.21	1.19	1.18	1.16	1.13	1.10
∞	1.32	1.39	1.37	1.35	1.33	1.31	1.29	1.28	1.27	1.25	1.24	1.22	1.19	1.18	1.16	1.14	1.12	1.08	1.00

Source: A portion of "Tables of percentage points of the inverted beta (F) distribution," Biometrika, 33 (1943) by M. Merrington and C. M. Thompson and from Table 18 of Biometrika Tables for Statisticians, Vol. 1, Cambridge University Press, 1954, edited by E. S. Pearson and H. O. Hartley. Reproduced with permission of authors, editors, and Biometrika trustees.

117

TABLE III (continued)

PERCENTAGE POINTS OF THE *F*-DISTRIBUTION

UPPER 10% POINTS

ν_2 \ ν_1	1	2	3	4	5	6	7	8	9	10	12	15	20	24	30	40	60	120	∞
1	39.86	49.50	53.59	55.83	57.24	58.20	58.91	59.44	59.86	60.19	60.71	61.22	61.74	62.00	62.26	62.53	62.79	63.06	63.33
2	8.53	9.00	9.16	9.24	9.29	9.33	9.35	9.37	9.38	9.39	9.41	9.42	9.44	9.45	9.46	9.47	9.47	9.48	9.49
3	5.54	5.46	5.39	5.34	5.31	5.28	5.27	5.25	5.24	5.23	5.22	5.20	5.18	5.18	5.17	5.16	5.15	5.14	5.13
4	4.54	4.32	4.19	4.11	4.05	4.01	3.98	3.95	3.94	3.92	3.90	3.87	3.84	3.83	3.82	3.80	3.79	3.78	3.76
5	4.06	3.78	3.62	3.52	3.45	3.40	3.37	3.34	3.32	3.30	3.27	3.24	3.21	3.19	3.17	3.16	3.14	3.12	3.10
6	3.78	3.46	3.29	3.18	3.11	3.05	3.01	2.98	2.96	2.94	2.90	2.87	2.84	2.82	2.80	2.78	2.76	2.74	2.72
7	3.59	3.26	3.07	2.96	2.88	2.83	2.78	2.75	2.72	2.70	2.67	2.63	2.59	2.58	2.56	2.54	2.51	2.49	2.47
8	3.46	3.11	2.92	2.81	2.73	2.67	2.62	2.59	2.56	2.54	2.50	2.46	2.42	2.40	2.38	2.36	2.34	2.32	2.29
9	3.36	3.01	2.81	2.69	2.61	2.55	2.51	2.47	2.44	2.42	2.38	2.34	2.30	2.28	2.25	2.23	2.21	2.18	2.16
10	3.29	2.92	2.73	2.61	2.52	2.46	2.41	2.38	2.35	2.32	2.28	2.24	2.20	2.18	2.16	2.13	2.11	2.08	2.06
11	3.23	2.86	2.66	2.54	2.45	2.39	2.34	2.30	2.27	2.25	2.21	2.17	2.12	2.10	2.08	2.05	2.03	2.00	1.97
12	3.18	2.81	2.61	2.48	2.39	2.33	2.28	2.24	2.21	2.19	2.15	2.10	2.06	2.04	2.01	1.99	1.96	1.93	1.90
13	3.14	2.76	2.56	2.43	2.35	2.28	2.23	2.20	2.16	2.14	2.10	2.05	2.01	1.98	1.96	1.93	1.90	1.88	1.85
14	3.10	2.73	2.52	2.39	2.31	2.24	2.19	2.15	2.12	2.10	2.05	2.01	1.96	1.94	1.91	1.89	1.86	1.83	1.80
15	3.07	2.70	2.49	2.36	2.27	2.21	2.16	2.12	2.09	2.06	2.02	1.97	1.92	1.90	1.87	1.85	1.82	1.79	1.76
16	3.05	2.67	2.46	2.33	2.24	2.18	2.13	2.09	2.06	2.03	1.99	1.94	1.89	1.87	1.84	1.81	1.78	1.75	1.72
17	3.03	2.64	2.44	2.31	2.22	2.15	2.10	2.06	2.03	2.00	1.96	1.91	1.86	1.84	1.81	1.78	1.75	1.72	1.69
18	3.01	2.62	2.42	2.29	2.20	2.13	2.08	2.04	2.00	1.98	1.93	1.89	1.84	1.81	1.78	1.75	1.72	1.69	1.66
19	2.99	2.61	2.40	2.27	2.18	2.11	2.06	2.02	1.98	1.96	1.91	1.86	1.81	1.79	1.76	1.73	1.70	1.67	1.63
20	2.97	2.59	2.38	2.25	2.16	2.09	2.04	2.00	1.96	1.94	1.89	1.84	1.79	1.77	1.74	1.71	1.68	1.64	1.61
21	2.96	2.57	2.36	2.23	2.14	2.08	2.02	1.98	1.95	1.92	1.87	1.83	1.78	1.75	1.72	1.69	1.66	1.62	1.59
22	2.95	2.56	2.35	2.22	2.13	2.06	2.01	1.97	1.93	1.90	1.86	1.81	1.76	1.73	1.70	1.67	1.64	1.60	1.57
23	2.94	2.55	2.34	2.21	2.11	2.05	1.99	1.95	1.92	1.89	1.84	1.80	1.74	1.72	1.69	1.66	1.62	1.59	1.55
24	2.93	2.54	2.33	2.19	2.10	2.04	1.98	1.94	1.91	1.88	1.83	1.78	1.73	1.70	1.67	1.64	1.61	1.57	1.53
25	2.92	2.53	2.32	2.18	2.09	2.02	1.97	1.93	1.89	1.87	1.82	1.77	1.72	1.69	1.66	1.63	1.59	1.56	1.52
26	2.91	2.52	2.31	2.17	2.08	2.01	1.96	1.92	1.88	1.86	1.81	1.76	1.71	1.68	1.65	1.61	1.58	1.54	1.50
27	2.90	2.51	2.30	2.17	2.07	2.00	1.95	1.91	1.87	1.85	1.80	1.75	1.70	1.67	1.64	1.60	1.57	1.53	1.49
28	2.89	2.50	2.29	2.16	2.06	2.00	1.94	1.90	1.87	1.84	1.79	1.74	1.69	1.66	1.63	1.59	1.56	1.52	1.48
29	2.89	2.50	2.28	2.15	2.06	1.99	1.93	1.89	1.86	1.83	1.78	1.73	1.68	1.65	1.62	1.58	1.55	1.51	1.47
30	2.88	2.49	2.28	2.14	2.05	1.98	1.93	1.88	1.85	1.82	1.77	1.72	1.67	1.64	1.61	1.57	1.54	1.50	1.46
40	2.84	2.44	2.23	2.09	2.00	1.93	1.87	1.83	1.79	1.76	1.71	1.66	1.61	1.57	1.54	1.51	1.47	1.42	1.38
60	2.79	2.39	2.18	2.04	1.95	1.87	1.82	1.77	1.74	1.71	1.66	1.60	1.54	1.51	1.48	1.44	1.40	1.35	1.29
120	2.75	2.35	2.13	1.99	1.90	1.82	1.77	1.72	1.68	1.65	1.60	1.55	1.48	1.45	1.41	1.37	1.32	1.26	1.19
∞	2.71	2.30	2.08	1.94	1.85	1.77	1.72	1.67	1.63	1.60	1.55	1.49	1.42	1.38	1.34	1.30	1.24	1.17	1.00

TABLE III (continued)

PERCENTAGE POINTS OF THE F-DISTRIBUTION

Upper 5% Points

$\nu_2 \backslash \nu_1$	1	2	3	4	5	6	7	8	9	10	12	15	20	24	30	40	60	120	∞
1	161.4	199.5	215.7	224.6	230.2	234.0	236.8	238.9	240.5	241.9	243.9	245.9	248.0	249.1	250.1	251.1	252.2	253.3	254.3
2	18.51	19.00	19.16	19.25	19.30	19.33	19.35	19.37	19.38	19.40	19.41	19.43	19.45	19.45	19.46	19.47	19.48	19.49	19.50
3	10.13	9.55	9.28	9.12	9.01	8.94	8.89	8.85	8.81	8.79	8.74	8.70	8.66	8.64	8.62	8.59	8.57	8.55	8.53
4	7.71	6.94	6.59	6.39	6.26	6.16	6.09	6.04	6.00	5.96	5.91	5.86	5.80	5.77	5.75	5.72	5.69	5.66	5.63
5	6.61	5.79	5.41	5.19	5.05	4.95	4.88	4.82	4.77	4.74	4.68	4.62	4.56	4.53	4.50	4.46	4.43	4.40	4.36
6	5.99	5.14	4.76	4.53	4.39	4.28	4.21	4.15	4.10	4.06	4.00	3.94	3.87	3.84	3.81	3.77	3.74	3.70	3.67
7	5.59	4.74	4.35	4.12	3.97	3.87	3.79	3.73	3.68	3.64	3.57	3.51	3.44	3.41	3.38	3.34	3.30	3.27	3.23
8	5.32	4.46	4.07	3.84	3.69	3.58	3.50	3.44	3.39	3.35	3.28	3.22	3.15	3.12	3.08	3.04	3.01	2.97	2.93
9	5.12	4.26	3.86	3.63	3.48	3.37	3.29	3.23	3.18	3.14	3.07	3.01	2.94	2.90	2.86	2.83	2.79	2.75	2.71
10	4.96	4.10	3.71	3.48	3.33	3.22	3.14	3.07	3.02	2.98	2.91	2.85	2.77	2.74	2.70	2.66	2.62	2.58	2.54
11	4.84	3.98	3.59	3.36	3.20	3.09	3.01	2.95	2.90	2.85	2.79	2.72	2.65	2.61	2.57	2.53	2.49	2.45	2.40
12	4.75	3.89	3.49	3.26	3.11	3.00	2.91	2.85	2.80	2.75	2.69	2.62	2.54	2.51	2.47	2.43	2.38	2.34	2.30
13	4.67	3.81	3.41	3.18	3.03	2.92	2.83	2.77	2.71	2.67	2.60	2.53	2.46	2.42	2.38	2.34	2.30	2.25	2.21
14	4.60	3.74	3.34	3.11	2.96	2.85	2.76	2.70	2.65	2.60	2.53	2.46	2.39	2.35	2.31	2.27	2.22	2.18	2.13
15	4.54	3.68	3.29	3.06	2.90	2.79	2.71	2.64	2.59	2.54	2.48	2.40	2.33	2.29	2.25	2.20	2.16	2.11	2.07
16	4.49	3.63	3.24	3.01	2.85	2.74	2.66	2.59	2.54	2.49	2.42	2.35	2.28	2.24	2.19	2.15	2.11	2.06	2.01
17	4.45	3.59	3.20	2.96	2.81	2.70	2.61	2.55	2.49	2.45	2.38	2.31	2.23	2.19	2.15	2.10	2.06	2.01	1.96
18	4.41	3.55	3.16	2.93	2.77	2.66	2.58	2.51	2.46	2.41	2.34	2.27	2.19	2.15	2.11	2.06	2.02	1.97	1.92
19	4.38	3.52	3.13	2.90	2.74	2.63	2.54	2.48	2.42	2.38	2.31	2.23	2.16	2.11	2.07	2.03	1.98	1.93	1.88
20	4.35	3.49	3.10	2.87	2.71	2.60	2.51	2.45	2.39	2.35	2.28	2.20	2.12	2.08	2.04	1.99	1.95	1.90	1.84
21	4.32	3.47	3.07	2.84	2.68	2.57	2.49	2.42	2.37	2.32	2.25	2.18	2.10	2.05	2.01	1.96	1.92	1.87	1.81
22	4.30	3.44	3.05	2.82	2.66	2.55	2.46	2.40	2.34	2.30	2.23	2.15	2.07	2.03	1.98	1.94	1.89	1.84	1.78
23	4.28	3.42	3.03	2.80	2.64	2.53	2.44	2.37	2.32	2.27	2.20	2.13	2.05	2.01	1.96	1.91	1.86	1.81	1.76
24	4.26	3.40	3.01	2.78	2.62	2.51	2.42	2.36	2.30	2.25	2.18	2.11	2.03	1.98	1.94	1.89	1.84	1.79	1.73
25	4.24	3.39	2.99	2.76	2.60	2.49	2.40	2.34	2.28	2.24	2.16	2.09	2.01	1.96	1.92	1.87	1.82	1.77	1.71
26	4.23	3.37	2.98	2.74	2.59	2.47	2.39	2.32	2.27	2.22	2.15	2.07	1.99	1.95	1.90	1.85	1.80	1.75	1.69
27	4.21	3.35	2.96	2.73	2.57	2.46	2.37	2.31	2.25	2.20	2.13	2.06	1.97	1.93	1.88	1.84	1.79	1.73	1.67
28	4.20	3.34	2.95	2.71	2.56	2.45	2.36	2.29	2.24	2.19	2.12	2.04	1.96	1.91	1.87	1.82	1.77	1.71	1.65
29	4.18	3.33	2.93	2.70	2.55	2.43	2.35	2.28	2.22	2.18	2.10	2.03	1.94	1.90	1.85	1.81	1.75	1.70	1.64
30	4.17	3.32	2.92	2.69	2.53	2.42	2.33	2.27	2.21	2.16	2.09	2.01	1.93	1.89	1.84	1.79	1.74	1.68	1.62
40	4.08	3.23	2.84	2.61	2.45	2.34	2.25	2.18	2.12	2.08	2.00	1.92	1.84	1.79	1.74	1.69	1.64	1.58	1.51
60	4.00	3.15	2.76	2.53	2.37	2.25	2.17	2.10	2.04	1.99	1.92	1.84	1.75	1.70	1.65	1.59	1.53	1.47	1.39
120	3.92	3.07	2.68	2.45	2.29	2.17	2.09	2.02	1.96	1.91	1.83	1.75	1.66	1.61	1.55	1.50	1.43	1.35	1.25
∞	3.84	3.00	2.60	2.37	2.21	2.10	2.01	1.94	1.88	1.83	1.75	1.67	1.57	1.52	1.46	1.39	1.32	1.22	1.00

TABLE III (continued)

PERCENTAGE POINTS OF THE F-DISTRIBUTION
UPPER 2.5% POINTS

ν_2 \ ν_1	1	2	3	4	5	6	7	8	9	10	12	15	20	24	30	40	60	120	∞
1	647.8	799.5	864.2	839.6	921.8	937.1	948.2	956.7	963.3	968.6	976.7	984.9	993.1	997.2	1001	1006	1010	1014	1018
2	38.51	39.00	39.17	39.25	39.30	39.33	39.36	39.37	39.39	39.40	39.41	39.43	39.45	39.46	39.46	39.47	39.48	39.49	39.50
3	17.44	16.04	15.44	15.10	14.88	14.73	14.62	14.54	14.47	14.42	14.34	14.25	14.17	14.12	14.08	14.04	13.99	13.95	13.90
4	12.22	10.65	9.98	9.60	9.36	9.20	9.07	8.98	8.90	8.84	8.75	8.66	8.56	8.51	8.46	8.41	8.36	8.31	8.26
5	10.01	8.43	7.76	7.39	7.15	6.98	6.85	6.76	6.68	6.62	6.52	6.43	6.33	6.28	6.23	6.18	6.12	6.07	6.02
6	8.81	7.26	6.60	6.23	5.99	5.82	5.70	5.60	5.52	5.46	5.37	5.27	5.17	5.12	5.07	5.01	4.96	4.90	4.85
7	8.07	6.54	5.89	5.52	5.29	5.12	4.99	4.90	4.82	4.76	4.67	4.57	4.47	4.42	4.36	4.31	4.25	4.20	4.14
8	7.57	6.06	5.42	5.05	4.82	4.65	4.53	4.43	4.36	4.30	4.20	4.10	4.00	3.95	3.89	3.84	3.78	3.73	3.67
9	7.21	5.71	5.08	4.72	4.48	4.32	4.20	4.10	4.03	3.96	3.87	3.77	3.67	3.61	3.56	3.51	3.45	3.39	3.33
10	6.94	5.46	4.83	4.47	4.24	4.07	3.95	3.85	3.78	3.72	3.62	3.52	3.42	3.37	3.31	3.26	3.20	3.14	3.08
11	6.72	5.26	4.63	4.28	4.04	3.88	3.76	3.66	3.59	3.53	3.43	3.33	3.23	3.17	3.12	3.06	3.00	2.94	2.88
12	6.55	5.10	4.47	4.12	3.89	3.73	3.61	3.51	3.44	3.37	3.28	3.18	3.07	3.02	2.96	2.91	2.85	2.79	2.72
13	6.41	4.97	4.35	4.00	3.77	3.60	3.48	3.39	3.31	3.25	3.15	3.05	2.95	2.89	2.84	2.78	2.72	2.66	2.60
14	6.30	4.86	4.24	3.89	3.66	3.50	3.38	3.29	3.21	3.15	3.05	2.95	2.84	2.79	2.73	2.67	2.61	2.55	2.49
15	6.20	4.77	4.15	3.80	3.58	3.41	3.29	3.20	3.12	3.06	2.96	2.86	2.76	2.70	2.64	2.59	2.52	2.46	2.40
16	6.12	4.69	4.08	3.73	3.50	3.34	3.22	3.12	3.05	2.99	2.89	2.79	2.68	2.63	2.57	2.51	2.45	2.38	2.32
17	6.04	4.62	4.01	3.66	3.44	3.28	3.16	3.06	2.98	2.92	2.82	2.72	2.62	2.56	2.50	2.44	2.38	2.32	2.25
18	5.98	4.56	3.95	3.61	3.38	3.22	3.10	3.01	2.93	2.87	2.77	2.67	2.56	2.50	2.44	2.38	2.32	2.26	2.19
19	5.92	4.51	3.90	3.56	3.33	3.17	3.05	2.96	2.88	2.82	2.72	2.62	2.51	2.45	2.39	2.33	2.27	2.20	2.13
20	5.87	4.46	3.86	3.51	3.29	3.13	3.01	2.91	2.84	2.77	2.68	2.57	2.46	2.41	2.35	2.29	2.22	2.16	2.09
21	5.83	4.42	3.82	3.48	3.25	3.09	2.97	2.87	2.80	2.73	2.64	2.53	2.42	2.37	2.31	2.25	2.18	2.11	2.04
22	5.79	4.38	3.78	3.44	3.22	3.05	2.93	2.84	2.76	2.70	2.60	2.50	2.39	2.33	2.27	2.21	2.14	2.08	2.00
23	5.75	4.35	3.75	3.41	3.18	3.02	2.90	2.81	2.73	2.67	2.57	2.47	2.36	2.30	2.24	2.18	2.11	2.04	1.97
24	5.72	4.32	3.72	3.38	3.15	2.99	2.87	2.78	2.70	2.64	2.54	2.44	2.33	2.27	2.21	2.15	2.08	2.01	1.94
25	5.69	4.29	3.69	3.35	3.13	2.97	2.85	2.75	2.68	2.61	2.51	2.41	2.30	2.24	2.18	2.12	2.05	1.98	1.91
26	5.66	4.27	3.67	3.33	3.10	2.94	2.82	2.73	2.65	2.59	2.49	2.39	2.28	2.22	2.16	2.09	2.03	1.95	1.88
27	5.63	4.24	3.65	3.31	3.08	2.92	2.80	2.71	2.63	2.57	2.47	2.36	2.25	2.19	2.13	2.07	2.00	1.93	1.85
28	5.61	4.22	3.63	3.29	3.06	2.90	2.78	2.69	2.61	2.55	2.45	2.34	2.23	2.17	2.11	2.05	1.98	1.91	1.83
29	5.59	4.20	3.61	3.27	3.04	2.88	2.76	2.67	2.59	2.53	2.43	2.32	2.21	2.15	2.09	2.03	1.96	1.89	1.81
30	5.57	4.18	3.59	3.25	3.03	2.87	2.75	2.65	2.57	2.51	2.41	2.31	2.20	2.14	2.07	2.01	1.94	1.87	1.79
40	5.42	4.05	3.46	3.13	2.90	2.74	2.62	2.53	2.45	2.39	2.29	2.18	2.07	2.01	1.94	1.88	1.80	1.72	1.64
60	5.29	3.93	3.34	3.01	2.79	2.63	2.51	2.41	2.33	2.27	2.17	2.06	1.94	1.88	1.82	1.74	1.67	1.58	1.48
120	5.15	3.80	3.23	2.89	2.67	2.52	2.39	2.30	2.22	2.16	2.05	1.94	1.82	1.76	1.69	1.61	1.53	1.43	1.31
∞	5.02	3.69	3.12	2.79	2.57	2.41	2.29	2.19	2.11	2.05	1.94	1.83	1.71	1.64	1.57	1.48	1.39	1.27	1.00

TABLE III (continued)

PERCENTAGE POINTS OF THE F-DISTRIBUTION
UPPER 1% POINTS

ν_2 \ ν_1	1	2	3	4	5	6	7	8	9	10	12	15	20	24	30	40	60	120	∞
1	4052	4999.5	5403	5625	5764	5859	5928	5982	6022	6056	6106	6157	6209	6235	6261	6287	6313	6339	6366
2	98.50	99.00	99.17	99.25	99.30	99.33	99.36	99.37	99.39	99.40	99.42	99.43	99.45	99.46	99.47	99.47	99.48	99.49	99.50
3	34.12	30.82	29.46	28.71	28.24	27.91	27.67	27.49	27.35	27.23	27.05	26.87	26.69	26.60	26.50	26.41	26.32	26.22	26.13
4	21.20	18.00	16.69	15.98	15.52	15.21	14.98	14.80	14.66	14.55	14.37	14.20	14.02	13.93	13.84	13.75	13.65	13.56	13.46
5	16.26	13.27	12.06	11.39	10.97	10.67	10.46	10.29	10.16	10.05	9.89	9.72	9.55	9.47	9.38	9.29	9.20	9.11	9.02
6	13.75	10.92	9.78	9.15	8.75	8.47	8.26	8.10	7.98	7.87	7.72	7.56	7.40	7.31	7.23	7.14	7.06	6.97	6.88
7	12.25	9.55	8.45	7.85	7.46	7.19	6.99	6.84	6.72	6.62	6.47	6.31	6.16	6.07	5.99	5.91	5.82	5.74	5.65
8	11.26	8.65	7.59	7.01	6.63	6.37	6.18	6.03	5.91	5.81	5.67	5.52	5.36	5.28	5.20	5.12	5.03	4.95	4.86
9	10.56	8.02	6.99	6.42	6.06	5.80	5.61	5.47	5.35	5.26	5.11	4.96	4.81	4.73	4.65	4.57	4.48	4.40	4.31
10	10.04	7.56	6.55	5.99	5.64	5.39	5.20	5.06	4.94	4.85	4.71	4.56	4.41	4.33	4.25	4.17	4.08	4.00	3.91
11	9.65	7.21	6.22	5.67	5.32	5.07	4.89	4.74	4.63	4.54	4.40	4.25	4.10	4.02	3.94	3.86	3.78	3.69	3.60
12	9.33	6.93	5.95	5.41	5.06	4.82	4.64	4.50	4.39	4.30	4.16	4.01	3.86	3.78	3.70	3.62	3.54	3.45	3.36
13	9.07	6.70	5.74	5.21	4.86	4.62	4.44	4.30	4.19	4.10	3.96	3.82	3.66	3.59	3.51	3.43	3.34	3.25	3.17
14	8.86	6.51	5.56	5.04	4.69	4.46	4.28	4.14	4.03	3.94	3.80	3.66	3.51	3.43	3.35	3.27	3.18	3.09	3.00
15	8.68	6.36	5.42	4.89	4.56	4.32	4.14	4.00	3.89	3.80	3.67	3.52	3.37	3.29	3.21	3.13	3.05	2.96	2.87
16	8.53	6.23	5.29	4.77	4.44	4.20	4.03	3.89	3.78	3.69	3.55	3.41	3.26	3.18	3.10	3.02	2.93	2.84	2.75
17	8.40	6.11	5.18	4.67	4.34	4.10	3.93	3.79	3.68	3.59	3.46	3.31	3.16	3.08	3.00	2.92	2.83	2.75	2.65
18	8.29	6.01	5.09	4.58	4.25	4.01	3.84	3.71	3.60	3.51	3.37	3.23	3.08	3.00	2.92	2.84	2.75	2.66	2.57
19	8.18	5.93	5.01	4.50	4.17	3.94	3.77	3.63	3.52	3.43	3.30	3.15	3.00	2.92	2.84	2.76	2.67	2.58	2.49
20	8.10	5.85	4.94	4.43	4.10	3.87	3.70	3.56	3.46	3.37	3.23	3.09	2.94	2.86	2.78	2.69	2.61	2.52	2.42
21	8.02	5.78	4.87	4.37	4.04	3.81	3.64	3.51	3.40	3.31	3.17	3.03	2.88	2.80	2.72	2.64	2.55	2.46	2.36
22	7.95	5.72	4.82	4.31	3.99	3.76	3.59	3.45	3.35	3.26	3.12	2.98	2.83	2.75	2.67	2.58	2.50	2.40	2.31
23	7.88	5.66	4.76	4.26	3.94	3.71	3.54	3.41	3.30	3.21	3.07	2.93	2.78	2.70	2.62	2.54	2.45	2.35	2.26
24	7.82	5.61	4.72	4.22	3.90	3.67	3.50	3.36	3.26	3.17	3.03	2.89	2.74	2.66	2.58	2.49	2.40	2.31	2.21
25	7.77	5.57	4.68	4.18	3.85	3.63	3.46	3.32	3.22	3.13	2.99	2.85	2.70	2.62	2.54	2.45	2.36	2.27	2.17
26	7.72	5.53	4.64	4.14	3.82	3.59	3.42	3.29	3.18	3.09	2.96	2.81	2.66	2.58	2.50	2.42	2.33	2.23	2.13
27	7.68	5.49	4.60	4.11	3.78	3.56	3.39	3.26	3.15	3.06	2.93	2.78	2.63	2.55	2.47	2.38	2.29	2.20	2.10
28	7.64	5.45	4.57	4.07	3.75	3.53	3.36	3.23	3.12	3.03	2.90	2.75	2.60	2.52	2.44	2.35	2.26	2.17	2.06
29	7.60	5.42	4.54	4.04	3.73	3.50	3.33	3.20	3.09	3.00	2.87	2.73	2.57	2.49	2.41	2.33	2.23	2.14	2.03
30	7.56	5.39	4.51	4.02	3.70	3.47	3.30	3.17	3.07	2.98	2.84	2.70	2.55	2.47	2.39	2.30	2.21	2.11	2.01
40	7.31	5.18	4.31	3.83	3.51	3.29	3.12	2.99	2.89	2.80	2.66	2.52	2.37	2.29	2.20	2.11	2.02	1.92	1.80
60	7.08	4.98	4.13	3.65	3.34	3.12	2.95	2.82	2.72	2.63	2.50	2.35	2.20	2.12	2.03	1.94	1.84	1.73	1.60
120	6.85	4.79	3.95	3.48	3.17	2.96	2.79	2.66	2.56	2.47	2.34	2.19	2.03	1.95	1.86	1.76	1.66	1.53	1.38
∞	6.63	4.61	3.78	3.32	3.02	2.80	2.64	2.51	2.41	2.32	2.18	2.04	1.88	1.79	1.70	1.59	1.47	1.32	1.00

TABLE III (continued)

PERCENTAGE POINTS OF THE F-DISTRIBUTION
UPPER 0.5% POINTS

ν_2 \ ν_1	1	2	3	4	5	6	7	8	9	10	12	15	20	24	30	40	60	120	∞
1	16211	20000	21615	22500	23056	23437	23715	23925	24091	24224	24426	24630	24836	24940	25044	25148	25253	25359	25465
2	198.5	199.0	199.2	199.2	199.3	199.3	199.4	199.4	199.4	199.4	199.4	199.4	199.4	199.5	199.5	199.5	199.5	199.5	199.5
3	55.55	49.80	47.47	46.19	45.39	44.84	44.43	44.13	43.88	43.69	43.39	43.08	42.78	42.62	42.47	42.31	42.15	41.99	41.83
4	31.33	26.28	24.26	23.15	22.46	21.97	21.62	21.35	21.14	20.97	20.70	20.44	20.17	20.03	19.89	19.75	19.61	19.47	19.32
5	22.78	18.31	16.53	15.56	14.94	14.51	14.20	13.96	13.77	13.62	13.38	13.15	12.90	12.78	12.66	12.53	12.40	12.27	12.14
6	18.63	14.54	12.92	12.03	11.46	11.07	10.79	10.57	10.39	10.25	10.03	9.81	9.59	9.47	9.36	9.24	9.12	9.00	8.88
7	16.24	12.40	10.88	10.05	9.52	9.16	8.89	8.68	8.51	8.38	8.18	7.97	7.75	7.65	7.53	7.42	7.31	7.19	7.08
8	14.69	11.04	9.60	8.81	8.30	7.95	7.69	7.50	7.34	7.21	7.01	6.81	6.61	6.50	6.40	6.29	6.18	6.06	5.95
9	13.61	10.11	8.72	7.96	7.47	7.13	6.88	6.69	6.54	6.42	6.23	6.03	5.83	5.73	5.62	5.52	5.41	5.30	5.19
10	12.83	9.43	8.08	7.34	6.87	6.54	6.30	6.12	5.97	5.85	5.66	5.47	5.27	5.17	5.07	4.97	4.86	4.75	4.64
11	12.23	8.91	7.60	6.88	6.42	6.10	5.86	5.68	5.54	5.42	5.24	5.05	4.86	4.76	4.65	4.55	4.44	4.34	4.23
12	11.75	8.51	7.23	6.52	6.07	5.76	5.52	5.35	5.20	5.09	4.91	4.72	4.53	4.43	4.33	4.23	4.12	4.01	3.90
13	11.37	8.19	6.93	6.23	5.79	5.48	5.25	5.08	4.94	4.82	4.64	4.46	4.27	4.17	4.07	3.97	3.87	3.76	3.65
14	11.06	7.92	6.68	6.00	5.56	5.26	5.03	4.86	4.72	4.60	4.43	4.25	4.06	3.96	3.86	3.76	3.66	3.55	3.44
15	10.80	7.70	6.48	5.80	5.37	5.07	4.85	4.67	4.54	4.42	4.25	4.07	3.88	3.79	3.69	3.58	3.48	3.37	3.26
16	10.58	7.51	6.30	5.64	5.21	4.91	4.69	4.52	4.38	4.27	4.10	3.92	3.73	3.64	3.54	3.44	3.33	3.22	3.11
17	10.38	7.35	6.16	5.50	5.07	4.78	4.56	4.39	4.25	4.14	3.97	3.79	3.61	3.51	3.41	3.31	3.21	3.10	2.98
18	10.22	7.21	6.03	5.37	4.96	4.66	4.44	4.28	4.14	4.03	3.86	3.68	3.50	3.40	3.30	3.20	3.10	2.99	2.87
19	10.07	7.09	5.92	5.27	4.85	4.56	4.34	4.18	4.04	3.93	3.76	3.59	3.40	3.31	3.21	3.11	3.00	2.89	2.78
20	9.94	6.99	5.82	5.17	4.76	4.47	4.26	4.09	3.96	3.85	3.68	3.50	3.32	3.22	3.12	3.02	2.92	2.81	2.69
21	9.83	6.89	5.73	5.09	4.68	4.39	4.18	4.01	3.88	3.77	3.60	3.43	3.24	3.15	3.05	2.95	2.84	2.73	2.61
22	9.73	6.81	5.65	5.02	4.61	4.32	4.11	3.94	3.81	3.70	3.54	3.36	3.18	3.08	2.98	2.88	2.77	2.66	2.55
23	9.63	6.73	5.58	4.95	4.54	4.26	4.05	3.88	3.75	3.64	3.47	3.30	3.12	3.02	2.92	2.82	2.71	2.60	2.48
24	9.55	6.66	5.52	4.89	4.49	4.20	3.99	3.83	3.69	3.59	3.42	3.25	3.06	2.97	2.87	2.77	2.66	2.55	2.43
25	9.48	6.60	5.46	4.84	4.43	4.15	3.94	3.78	3.64	3.54	3.37	3.20	3.01	2.92	2.82	2.72	2.61	2.50	2.38
26	9.41	6.54	5.41	4.79	4.38	4.10	3.89	3.73	3.60	3.49	3.33	3.15	2.97	2.87	2.77	2.67	2.56	2.45	2.33
27	9.34	6.49	5.36	4.74	4.34	4.06	3.85	3.69	3.56	3.45	3.28	3.11	2.93	2.83	2.73	2.63	2.52	2.41	2.29
28	9.28	6.44	5.32	4.70	4.30	4.02	3.81	3.65	3.52	3.41	3.25	3.07	2.89	2.79	2.69	2.59	2.48	2.37	2.25
29	9.23	6.40	5.28	4.66	4.26	3.98	3.77	3.61	3.48	3.38	3.21	3.04	2.86	2.76	2.66	2.56	2.45	2.33	2.21
30	9.18	6.35	5.24	4.62	4.23	3.95	3.74	3.58	3.45	3.34	3.18	3.01	2.82	2.73	2.63	2.52	2.42	2.30	2.18
40	8.83	6.07	4.98	4.37	3.99	3.71	3.51	3.35	3.22	3.12	2.95	2.78	2.60	2.50	2.40	2.30	2.18	2.06	1.93
60	8.49	5.79	4.73	4.14	3.76	3.49	3.29	3.13	3.01	2.90	2.74	2.57	2.39	2.29	2.19	2.08	1.96	1.83	1.69
120	8.18	5.54	4.50	3.92	3.55	3.28	3.09	2.93	2.81	2.71	2.54	2.37	2.19	2.09	1.98	1.87	1.75	1.61	1.43
∞	7.88	5.30	4.28	3.72	3.35	3.09	2.90	2.74	2.62	2.52	2.36	2.19	2.00	1.90	1.79	1.67	1.53	1.36	1.00

TABLE IV

Upper Percentage Points of the Studentized Range, $q_z = \dfrac{\bar{x}_{max} - \bar{x}_{min}}{s_{\bar{x}}}$

Upper 5% Points

p = number of treatment means

Error df	2	3	4	5	6	7	8	9	10	11	12	13	14	15	16	17	18	19	20
1	18.0	27.0	32.8	37.1	40.4	43.1	45.4	47.4	49.1	50.6	52.0	53.2	54.3	55.4	56.3	57.2	58.0	58.8	59.6
2	6.09	8.3	9.8	10.9	11.7	12.4	13.0	13.5	14.0	14.4	14.7	15.1	15.4	15.7	15.9	16.1	16.4	16.6	16.8
3	4.50	5.91	6.82	7.50	8.04	8.48	8.85	9.18	9.46	9.72	9.95	10.15	10.35	10.52	10.69	10.84	10.98	11.11	11.24
4	3.93	5.04	5.76	6.29	6.71	7.05	7.35	7.60	7.83	8.03	8.21	8.37	8.52	8.66	8.79	8.91	9.03	9.13	9.23
5	3.63	4.60	5.22	5.67	6.03	6.33	6.58	6.80	6.99	7.17	7.32	7.47	7.60	7.72	7.83	7.93	8.03	8.12	8.21
6	3.46	4.34	4.90	5.31	5.63	5.89	6.12	6.32	6.49	6.65	6.79	6.92	7.03	7.14	7.24	7.34	7.43	7.51	7.59
7	3.34	4.16	4.68	5.06	5.36	5.61	5.82	6.00	6.16	6.30	6.43	6.55	6.66	6.76	6.85	6.94	7.02	7.09	7.17
8	3.26	4.04	4.53	4.89	5.17	5.40	5.60	5.77	5.92	6.05	6.18	6.29	6.39	6.48	6.57	6.65	6.73	6.80	6.87
9	3.20	3.95	4.42	4.76	5.02	5.24	5.43	5.60	5.74	5.87	5.98	6.09	6.19	6.28	6.36	6.44	6.51	6.58	6.64
10	3.15	3.88	4.33	4.65	4.91	5.12	5.30	5.46	5.60	5.72	5.83	5.93	6.03	6.11	6.20	6.27	6.34	6.40	6.47
11	3.11	3.82	4.26	4.57	4.82	5.03	5.20	5.35	5.49	5.61	5.71	5.81	5.90	5.99	6.06	6.14	6.20	6.26	6.33
12	3.08	3.77	4.20	4.51	4.75	4.95	5.12	5.27	5.40	5.51	5.62	5.71	5.80	5.88	5.95	6.03	6.09	6.15	6.21
13	3.06	3.73	4.15	4.45	4.69	4.88	5.05	5.19	5.32	5.43	5.53	5.63	5.71	5.79	5.86	5.93	6.00	6.05	6.11
14	3.03	3.70	4.11	4.41	4.64	4.83	4.99	5.13	5.25	5.36	5.46	5.55	5.64	5.72	5.79	5.85	5.92	5.97	6.03
15	3.01	3.67	4.08	4.37	4.60	4.78	4.94	5.08	5.20	5.31	5.40	5.49	5.58	5.65	5.72	5.79	5.85	5.90	5.96
16	3.00	3.65	4.05	4.33	4.56	4.74	4.90	5.03	5.15	5.26	5.35	5.44	5.52	5.59	5.66	5.72	5.79	5.84	5.90
17	2.98	3.63	4.02	4.30	4.52	4.71	4.86	4.99	5.11	5.21	5.31	5.39	5.47	5.55	5.61	5.68	5.74	5.79	5.84
18	2.97	3.61	4.00	4.28	4.49	4.67	4.82	4.96	5.07	5.17	5.27	5.35	5.43	5.50	5.57	5.63	5.69	5.74	5.79
19	2.96	3.59	3.98	4.25	4.47	4.65	4.79	4.92	5.04	5.14	5.23	5.32	5.39	5.46	5.53	5.59	5.65	5.70	5.75
20	2.95	3.58	3.96	4.23	4.45	4.62	4.77	4.90	5.01	5.11	5.20	5.28	5.36	5.43	5.49	5.55	5.61	5.66	5.71
24	2.92	3.53	3.90	4.17	4.37	4.54	4.68	4.81	4.92	5.01	5.10	5.18	5.25	5.32	5.38	5.44	5.50	5.54	5.59
30	2.89	3.49	3.84	4.10	4.30	4.46	4.60	4.72	4.83	4.92	5.00	5.08	5.15	5.21	5.27	5.33	5.38	5.43	5.48
40	2.86	3.44	3.79	4.04	4.23	4.39	4.52	4.63	4.74	4.82	4.91	4.98	5.05	5.11	5.16	5.22	5.27	5.31	5.36
60	2.83	3.40	3.74	3.98	4.16	4.31	4.44	4.55	4.65	4.73	4.81	4.88	4.94	5.00	5.06	5.11	5.16	5.20	5.24
120	2.80	3.36	3.69	3.92	4.10	4.24	4.36	4.48	4.56	4.64	4.72	4.78	4.84	4.90	4.95	5.00	5.05	5.09	5.13
∞	2.77	3.31	3.63	3.86	4.03	4.17	4.29	4.39	4.47	4.55	4.62	4.68	4.74	4.80	4.85	4.89	4.93	4.97	5.01

Source: This table is abridged from Table 29, *Biometrika Tables for Statisticians*, Vol. 1, Cambridge University Press, 1954. It is reproduced with permission of the *Biometrika* trustees and the editors, E. S. Pearson and H. O. Hartley. The original work appeared in a paper by J. M. May, "Extended and corrected tables of the upper percentage points of the 'Studentized' range," *Biometrika*, 39:192–193 (1952).

TABLE IV (continued)

Upper Percentage Points of the Studentized Range, $q_x = \dfrac{\bar{x}_{max} - \bar{x}_{min}}{s_{\bar{x}}}$

Upper 1% Points

Error df	p = number of treatment means																		
	2	3	4	5	6	7	8	9	10	11	12	13	14	15	16	17	18	19	20
1	90.0	135	164	186	202	216	227	237	246	253	260	266	272	277	282	286	290	294	298
2	14.0	19.0	22.3	24.7	26.6	28.2	29.5	30.7	31.7	32.6	33.4	34.1	34.8	35.4	36.0	36.5	37.0	37.5	37.9
3	8.26	10.6	12.2	13.3	14.2	15.0	15.6	16.2	16.7	17.1	17.5	17.9	18.2	18.5	18.8	19.1	19.3	19.5	19.8
4	6.51	8.12	9.17	9.96	10.6	11.1	11.5	11.9	12.3	12.6	12.8	13.1	13.3	13.5	13.7	13.9	14.1	14.2	14.4
5	5.70	6.97	7.80	8.42	8.91	9.32	9.67	9.97	10.24	10.48	10.70	10.89	11.08	11.24	11.40	11.55	11.68	11.81	11.93
6	5.24	6.33	7.03	7.56	7.97	8.32	8.61	8.87	9.10	9.30	9.49	9.65	9.81	9.95	10.08	10.21	10.32	10.43	10.54
7	4.95	5.92	6.54	7.01	7.37	7.68	7.94	8.17	8.37	8.55	8.71	8.86	9.00	9.12	9.24	9.35	9.46	9.55	9.65
8	4.74	5.63	6.20	6.63	6.96	7.24	7.47	7.68	7.87	8.03	8.18	8.31	8.44	8.55	8.66	8.76	8.85	8.94	9.03
9	4.60	5.43	5.96	6.35	6.66	6.91	7.13	7.32	7.49	7.65	7.78	7.91	8.03	8.13	8.23	8.32	8.41	8.49	8.57
10	4.48	5.27	5.77	6.14	6.43	6.67	6.87	7.05	7.21	7.36	7.48	7.60	7.71	7.81	7.91	7.99	8.07	8.15	8.22
11	4.39	5.14	5.62	5.97	6.25	6.48	6.67	6.84	6.99	7.13	7.25	7.36	7.46	7.56	7.65	7.73	7.81	7.88	7.95
12	4.32	5.04	5.50	5.84	6.10	6.32	6.51	6.67	6.81	6.94	7.06	7.17	7.26	7.36	7.44	7.52	7.59	7.66	7.73
13	4.26	4.96	5.40	5.73	5.98	6.19	6.37	6.53	6.67	6.79	6.90	7.01	7.10	7.19	7.27	7.34	7.42	7.48	7.55
14	4.21	4.89	5.32	5.63	5.88	6.08	6.26	6.41	6.54	6.66	6.77	6.87	6.96	7.05	7.12	7.20	7.27	7.33	7.39
15	4.17	4.83	5.25	5.56	5.80	5.99	6.16	6.31	6.44	6.55	6.66	6.76	6.84	6.93	7.00	7.07	7.14	7.20	7.26
16	4.13	4.78	5.19	5.49	5.72	5.92	6.08	6.22	6.35	6.46	6.56	6.66	6.74	6.82	6.90	6.97	7.03	7.09	7.15
17	4.10	4.74	5.14	5.43	5.66	5.85	6.01	6.15	6.27	6.38	6.48	6.57	6.66	6.73	6.80	6.87	6.94	7.00	7.05
18	4.07	4.70	5.09	5.38	5.60	5.79	5.94	6.08	6.20	6.31	6.41	6.50	6.58	6.65	6.72	6.79	6.85	6.91	6.96
19	4.05	4.67	5.05	5.33	5.55	5.73	5.89	6.02	6.14	6.25	6.34	6.43	6.51	6.58	6.65	6.72	6.78	6.84	6.89
20	4.02	4.64	5.02	5.29	5.51	5.69	5.84	5.97	6.09	6.19	6.29	6.37	6.45	6.52	6.59	6.65	6.71	6.76	6.82
24	3.96	4.54	4.91	5.17	5.37	5.54	5.69	5.81	5.92	6.02	6.11	6.19	6.26	6.33	6.39	6.45	6.51	6.56	6.61
30	3.89	4.45	4.80	5.05	5.24	5.40	5.54	5.65	5.76	5.85	5.93	6.01	6.08	6.14	6.20	6.26	6.31	6.36	6.41
40	3.82	4.37	4.70	4.93	5.11	5.27	5.39	5.50	5.60	5.69	5.77	5.84	5.90	5.96	6.02	6.07	6.12	6.17	6.21
60	3.76	4.28	4.60	4.82	4.99	5.13	5.25	5.36	5.45	5.53	5.60	5.67	5.73	5.79	5.84	5.89	5.93	5.98	6.02
120	3.70	4.20	4.50	4.71	4.87	5.01	5.12	5.21	5.30	5.38	5.44	5.51	5.56	5.61	5.66	5.71	5.75	5.79	5.83
∞	3.64	4.12	4.40	4.60	4.76	4.88	4.99	5.08	5.16	5.23	5.29	5.35	5.40	5.45	5.49	5.54	5.57	5.61	5.65

124

Author Index

Subject Index